The
STRESS-BUSTER
Workbook

75 Evidence-Based Strategies to
Help Kids Regulate Their Emotions,
Build Coping Skills, and Tap into Positive Thinking

KATIE HURLEY, LCSW

Published by
PESI Publishing
3839 White Ave
Eau Claire, WI 54703

Cover: Amy Rubenzer
Editing: Jenessa Jackson, PhD
Layout: Baker & Taylor and Amy Rubenzer

9781683734420 (print)
9781683734437 (epub)
9781683734444 (epdf)

Printed in the United States of America.

PESI Publishing
pesipublishing.com

For Violet and Ella,
May the magic of play help you weather any storms you might encounter.

ABOUT THE AUTHOR

KATIE HURLEY, LCSW, is a child and adolescent psychotherapist, parenting educator, public speaker, and writer. She is the founder of "Girls Can!" empowerment groups for girls ages five to eleven. Hurley is the author of the award-winning *No More Mean Girls: The Secret to Raising Strong, Confident, and Compassionate Girls*; *The Depression Workbook for Teens: Tools to Improve Your Mood, Build Self-Esteem, and Stay Motivated*; *A Year of Positive Thinking for Teens: Daily Motivation to Beat Stress, Inspire Happiness, and Achieve Your Goals*; and *The Happy Kid Handbook: How to Raise Joyful Children in a Stressful World*. Hurley covers mental health, child and adolescent development, and parenting for *The Washington Post*, *PBS Parents*, *Psychology Today*, *Everyday Health*, *PsyCom*, and *U.S. News & World Report*, among other places.

She practices psychotherapy in the South Bay area of Los Angeles and earned her BA in psychology and women's studies from Boston College and her MSW from the University of Pennsylvania. She splits her time between Los Angeles and coastal Connecticut with her husband and two children.

TABLE OF CONTENTS

A LETTER TO THE KIDS

Dear Kids,

This book is for you! One thing I notice a lot lately is that kids have a ton of stress. Maybe school feels too hard, or sports seem too competitive, or making and keeping friends isn't as easy as you hoped. Those are a few examples, but kids just like you tell me all kinds of reasons why they feel stressed. I want you to know that experiencing stress is part of growing up. Everyone feels stressed at times, and everyone can learn how to manage stress.

This book will teach you to spot your own signs of stress and figure out what to do to feel better, how to overcome obstacles that frustrate you (we all have them!), how to share your feelings and needs with others, how to build your own self-confidence by believing in yourself, and how to use positive thinking to get through hard stuff. I bet that sounds like a lot, but I know you can do it.

You can read this book little by little or all at once. You can share it with a grown-up or keep it to yourself. When you finish this book, you'll be able to teach other kids, and even your grown-ups, everything you know about stress and how to manage it—you'll be an expert!

Even though feeling stressed might make you feel lonely at times, it's really important for you to know that you are definitely not alone. I hope that learning to work through your stress helps you feel more confident and happier.

Katie Hurley, LCSW

A LETTER TO THE GROWN-UPS

Dear Grown-Ups,

In over twenty-two years of direct practice with kids and teens, I've watched stress levels rise among younger children. In the early days of my career, the youngest children to enter my office needed social skills training or support because of a medical condition or some other environmental factor (loss, divorce, parent with cancer). Today, kids as young as five seek my help to manage feelings of stress and anxiety that overwhelm them on a daily basis. A lot has changed for young children over the course of my career, and I find that kids, and their parents, need support and specific strategies to target stress now more than ever.

The most frequently asked question I get from parents right now is "*How do I teach my child to handle stress and obstacles?*" From academics that are beyond a child's developmental level, to near-constant testing, to the expectation that kids specialize in a sport or other activity by early elementary school, the expectation gap (the gap between what parents think kids are capable of and what they are actually developmentally prepared for) appears to be growing at a fast pace, and that is contributing to increased stress. But even when I work with parents to help close that gap in the home, kids are growing up in a world that runs on stress. From bullying (even in kindergarten) and peer pressure, to natural disasters, school shootings, and COVID-19, modern kids face obstacles that can feel insurmountable.

How can we address all of these issues? By teaching kids how to endure uncomfortable emotions and manage stress as it occurs. That's where *The Stress-Buster Workbook for Kids* comes in. Using activities and scripts that I developed and tested with kids over the past twenty-two years, this book will help kids ages four to eleven learn to work through their stressors and cope with negative emotions.

Designed to offer a myriad of solutions—as we know that all kids are different and need strategies that work for them—*The Stress-Buster Workbook for Kids* is the perfect tool for parents, as well as teachers, therapists, and any other professionals working with young children. The exercises are easy to implement and effective, offering fast relief for stressed-out kids.

I hope this book allows you to better help the little ones in your lives. Though we are not all in the same boat on any given day, we can raft together to help one another stay afloat through difficult times. Please consider this a life jacket from me to you. One small floatation device to help you stay above the waterline through stormy seas.

Katie Hurley, LCSW

INTRODUCTION

Understanding Stress

How Do I Know If I Need This Book?

You learn a lot of different things in school, and chances are you have a favorite subject, but one thing schools don't have a ton of time to teach right now is stress management. Here's the thing: Even if you don't feel super stressed *right now*, a book like this can help you learn to cope so that the next time you feel stressed, you'll know what to do. The word *cope* is just another way of saying that you can get through a tough time—and coping skills will help you to do just that!

Every kid encounters some stress. It might be something at school, at home, in the news, or even on a team or during an extracurricular activity. The truth is, the obstacles that sometimes stress us out can also help us learn to work through hard things. So it's always a good time to have a book like this handy.

What Is Stress and How Do I Know If I Have It?

First things, first: Not all stress is bad. It's true! There's good stress, too, and that's the kind of stress that helps kids rise to challenges, work through conflict, and overcome problems. But when other kids (or your grown-ups!) say they feel stressed, they're not usually talking about good stress. It helps to understand more about how people experience stress so that you can learn to handle it.

These are the three kinds of stress you might encounter on any given day:

- **Good stress:** This happens when you encounter a situation that might feel scary, but you feel confident in your ability to manage it. Good stress makes us stronger because we can look back at the situation in the future and remember how we successfully got through it.

- **Tolerable stress:** This kind of stress occurs when you encounter something that feels a little scarier or threatening, but you're able to recognize that you've handled something like this before so you *can* get through it. Tolerable stress reminds us that we can overcome challenges, even if it feels hard to do in the moment. It builds our confidence even more when we work through the stressor.

- **Bad stress:** This occurs when we're in a threatening or scary situation that seems to keep going and going, and we don't know how to deal with it. Kids tend to freeze up when they encounter this kind of stress. You might feel helpless in the moment, and that can affect your self-confidence.

Let's discuss some examples!

Good Stress

Let's say you're skateboarding down a hill and picking up a lot of speed when you notice a group of small children crossing your path at the bottom of the hill. You know they don't see you coming, and your brain signals you to do something to avoid colliding with them. You slow down your board by leaning back on the tail and make a safe turn to the left or right to stop before you reach the children.

What happens during that encounter is that your brain shifts into survival mode. It signals different parts of your body to help you solve the problem, and you manage to avoid a collision. If you feel your heart racing during an incident like this, that's because your brain is telling your heart to pump more blood to your legs to slow that board down. It's also signaling you to steady your breathing and to use your vision to assess the situation. Brains know what to do when good stress occurs!

Tolerable Stress

Imagine that you take your younger sibling on a walk on a bright, sunny day. You decide to wander a little farther than usual because it's so nice out and you're enjoying the day. Suddenly a storm rolls in. It begins to rain, so you turn around and head for home. No big deal. Then you notice very dark clouds in the sky. Before you know it, you hear thunder off in the distance. You feel scared because you're still pretty far from home, the rain is pouring down, and you're worried about your sibling.

You probably feel more stressed in this example because this is a greater level of danger, but your brain knows what to do. You remember that you've been in situations like this before and that you can handle it. You pick up the pace and challenge your sibling to a race so you can make it home faster. You feel your heart racing as it pumps blood to your legs, and you remind yourself to take deep breaths as you run for home.

Bad Stress

What if, while you're running for home in the previous scenario, you see lightning slicing through the dark clouds and hear thunder rumbling overhead? You would likely feel *very* afraid if that happened, and you might not know what to do. Keep running? Head for cover? What if your sibling starts crying or starts panicking? How can you possibly help when you feel frozen with fear too?

This is an example of bad stress, which is physically and emotionally exhausting. It can cause your brain to think about only negative or bad outcomes, and it can make it hard to make decisions. This kind of stress can affect anyone, and it doesn't have to be a super-scary event like getting caught in a dangerous storm. You might feel this way when you get into an argument with a friend or when your schoolwork feels too hard.

The good news is that you can learn to manage these hard feelings and learn to take control in stressful situations. That's because all the previous descriptions of stress were examples of *situational stress*. That means there is a specific event or issue that causes your brain to go into what is called "fight-or-flight" mode. Your brain does this because it is always working hard to protect you, even when you're feeling scared! On the next page, you'll see what this fight-or-flight response involves.

FIGHT OR FLIGHT?

When your body senses any sort of threat or danger, it activates what is known as the stress response or the fight-or-flight response. This response prepares you to face the danger head-on (*fight*) or to run away if it seems too scary (*flight*). When this happens, your brain sends out an alert to your nervous system, and this causes a bunch of physical reactions to occur in your body. For example, your heart might start racing and you might start breathing pretty quickly. These reactions are intended to help you stay safe because they help you figure out how to respond to the threat!

Fight

Stand your ground.

Defend yourself.

Attack the problem.

Don't give up.

OR

Flight

Retreat!

Remove yourself.

Run away.

Move away from the threat.

Sometimes you can fight against the threat and get through it, but other times the best thing to do is to move away from the stressor and get help. You are not expected to handle every stressful situation on your own. No one can do that!

Can you think of a time when you experienced fight or flight? Write or draw about it here.

Triggers and Symptoms

Although some stress is situational, there will also be times when you experience ongoing stress and you're not really sure what the cause is. This is common among kids your age (and even for grown-ups too!), and there are a lot of things that can trigger stress. *Triggers* are things that push your stress buttons. This can happen when a whole bunch of little things add up over time, or it might be the same thing that happens over and over again.

There are two things that will help you know when you're feeling stressed: your triggers and your symptoms. In the table that follows, you'll find a list of common stress triggers for kids your age. Circle any that apply to you. I also left some blank boxes in case you need to add your own. Remember: Everyone is different, and we all have our own triggers! When you learn yours, you can figure out how to manage them.

Friendships	School	Big changes	Divorce
Family troubles	Illness	Loss	Separation anxiety
World news	Test anxiety	Busy schedule	Bullying
Screen time	Parent stress	Pressure to perform	New sibling
Peer pressure	Puberty	Not enough sleep	Loneliness

Kids are often busy with school and other activities, and that makes it hard to take the time to sit down and actually think about what stresses them out, but it's really important to find that time. Even though it's uncomfortable to think about what makes you feel stressed, it helps you learn important information about yourself. When you have that information, you can figure out a plan to cope with those triggers.

Symptoms of stress are another thing that can differ from kid to kid. If your friend tells you that stress causes them to have headaches, but you don't ever get headaches, that doesn't mean you've never felt stressed. That just means your symptoms might be different. Here are some common symptoms of stress that kids your age experience. Put a check mark by any you've experienced. And if you don't see your symptoms in the list, go ahead and add them at the end. If you really don't have any symptoms of stress, good for you! This book will still help you figure out strategies to use in case you need them in the future.

- ☐ Headaches

- ☐ Stomachaches

- ☐ Muscle aches

- ☐ Trouble sleeping

- ☑ Irritability (this means you feel super cranky)

- ☐ Nightmares

- ☐ Changes in eating habits (for example, not feeling hungry very often)

- ☐ Not wanting to participate in your usual stuff (school, sports, other programs)

- ☐ Trouble concentrating

- ☐ Not wanting to be with your friends

- ☑ Crying or feeling sad a lot but not knowing why

- ☐ _____

- ☐ _____

- ☐ _____

- ☐ _____

Let's Get to Work!

Now that you know your triggers and symptoms, it's time to put this book to work. You can read it in order or skip around. Each chapter focuses on a different topic that will help you build your coping skills and feel happier.

You might find that some strategies and ideas work better than others. That's okay. This book is designed to help all kids, so there are tons of activities and skills. I tried to offer a little bit of everything to help as many kids as possible.

It's important to try each strategy a few times before you move on, though. There are no instant fixes when it comes to coping with stress. You have to build your coping muscles, and the only way to do that is with practice! Give it time. I know we live in a fast-paced world right now, but slowing down will help you learn how to deal with big feelings.

CHAPTER ONE

What Is This Feeling?

Most kids know their basic feelings, such as happy, sad, mad, and scared. It's natural for kids of all ages to experience emotions that change throughout the day. While those basic emotions are a solid starting point, it's really important to build *emotional granularity*. This is just a fancy word that means you can understand a wide range (a lot!) of emotions and recognize that there are feelings within feelings.

That sounds confusing, I know. But consider a feeling like anger. What does it really mean when you say that you feel angry? Is it that you're really mad about something unfair that happened, or is there more to the story? It could mean that you feel left out, jealous, frustrated, annoyed, impatient, or irritated, to name a few emotions. Anger can represent a whole bunch of feelings mixed together into some sort of feelings soup!

Feelings Soup

Let's make a feelings soup. Pick a feeling, any feeling. I'll pick happy for mine. I'm making happy soup. The first thing I need to do is to think about what other feelings are similar to happiness. For example, sometimes when I feel really proud of myself or someone else, I notice that I smile a lot. When I'm in a silly or playful mood, I also feel really happy. To make the connections between my feelings, I like to close my eyes and imagine all the people and things that usually help me feel happy and say them out loud. Once I do that, I can think of all the feelings that pair with—or go along with—those feelings.

For my warm bowl of happy soup, my ingredients for happiness include feeling loved, silly, excited, proud, caring, and thoughtful.

It's your turn! Fill in your feelings soup flavor and add your ingredients to the bowl. Mix it up and see how many feelings are related to other feelings!

FEELINGS SOUP

Flavor: _____

Ingredients:

When you can name your feelings and share them with others, you can ask for help when you need it or use coping strategies to help you deal with that feeling. Developing emotional granularity is an important first step in learning to manage stress. Let's spend a little more time finding different ways to think about and understand emotions.

Feelings Check-In Board

Sometimes it's difficult to describe how you're feeling. That's okay. Everyone struggles with that sometimes. Having a check-in board with a list of emotions (including feelings faces) can help you identify how you're feeling. The example here shows a few emotions kids experience, but you can add as many as you want to your own check-in board. The more, the better!

Check in here!

Loved   Confused   Sad

Scared   Happy   Bored

Angry   Overwhelmed   Annoyed

Here are a few ways to create your own check-in board:

- Get a large poster board or piece of paper and draw your own feelings faces the way you imagine them to look.

- Take pictures of yourself making different feelings faces, print them, and cut and paste them onto the board.

- Print emojis or your favorite cartoon characters making feelings faces, and cut and paste them onto the board.

You can use sticky tabs to check in and share your feelings, or you can print pictures of each family member and use paperclips or thumbtacks to move them around each time you do a family check-in. Try to do this at least twice a day, and spend time talking about each person's feeling and why they feel that way. When families do this together, it makes it a lot easier to talk about feelings.

Feelings, Thoughts, and Needs

Three things that are always connected are your feelings, your thoughts, and your needs. When you experience a feeling (whether it's positive or negative), it affects your thinking. So if you experience anger, for example, you might start thinking that nothing is going right for you. In order to cope with the feeling, you have to figure out what you *need* to get through the situation.

Using a feelings, thoughts, and needs inventory gives you a chance to break down these three components into manageable parts so you can figure out what you need to do to cope. Let's practice by looking at the following example.

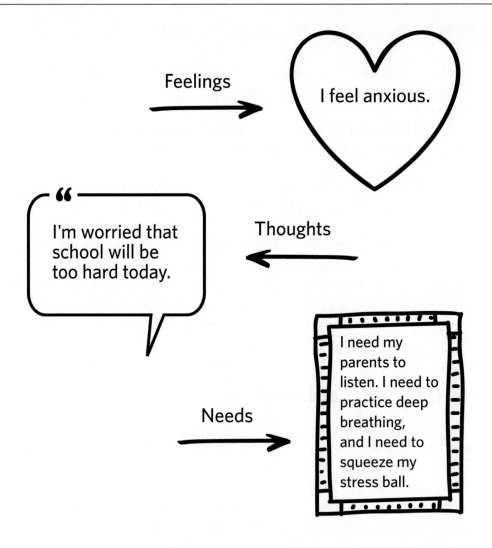

You can tell from the chart that this kid is feeling anxious. That anxiety is making them feel like school is too hard and like it's not a good day to go to school. This kid needs a parent who can listen and understand, they need to practice deep breathing, and they need a stress ball to bring to school to help them cope with their worries.

Now it's your turn!

FEELINGS, THOUGHTS, AND NEEDS

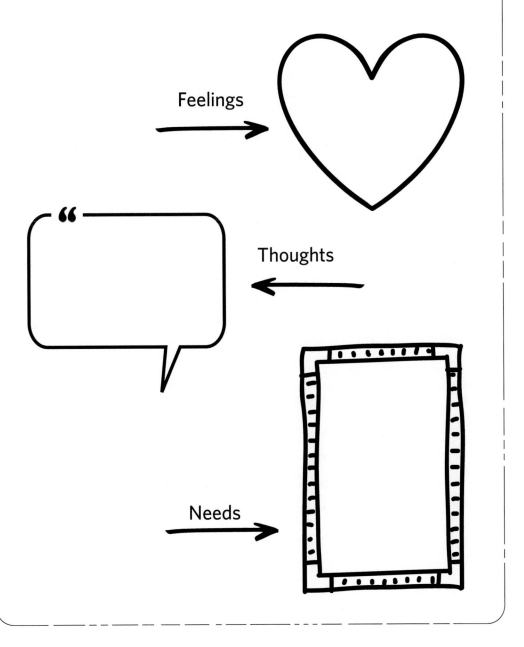

Feelings

Thoughts

Needs

Unmasking Feelings

Have you ever noticed that the feeling you show on the outside might not actually match the feeling on the inside? This can happen when frustration bubbles over, but then you find that you actually feel really sad. Or you might show sadness on the outside, when in reality, you feel lonely. Feelings can wear masks, and taking off the mask to see what's behind it helps us know what we're really dealing with.

Think of a time when you showed one emotion on the outside but felt something else on the inside. On the next page, fill in the masks to show your different feelings. Color in your masks to make them show your true feelings, and then write down what triggered you to feel this way.

UNMASKING FEELINGS

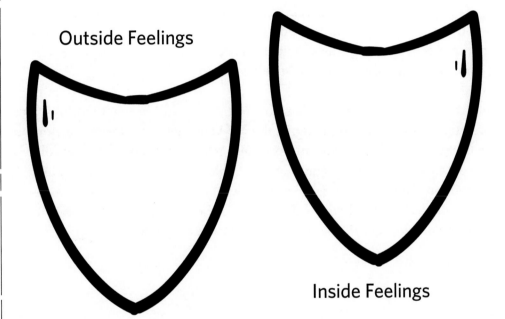

Outside Feelings

Inside Feelings

I think I felt this way because...

_____

_____

_____

_____

Color Your Day

Kids are really busy throughout the day, and most kids experience a whole bunch of emotions—both positive and negative—during this time. So when adults ask about feelings, it might be hard to narrow it down. That's okay!

Instead of trying to think about how you felt during one particular moment, it can be helpful to think about how you felt throughout the entire day. It can also help to break up your day into parts so you can remember how you felt at certain times. For example, you might think about how you felt before school or camp, how you felt before lunch, how you felt after lunch and in the afternoon, how you felt once you got home, and how you felt before bed. In fact, bedtime is a really good time to do this activity because it helps you get your feelings out, and coloring is actually a great stress reliever.

Think about your day today. I bet you felt a lot of different emotions today. Before you do anything else, assign colors to your feelings. You might think red is the best color for frustration, for example. You choose. Use the little color key on the activity page to keep track of what colors you want to correspond with each emotion. Now color in your day! How much of your day included feeling calm? Color that much of your calm color on the next page. How about feeling sad? Add that color too. Keep going until your day is full of color.

COLOR YOUR DAY

☀ Morning:

☀ Afternoon:

☾ Evening:

Color Key

Red = Pissed off

Orange = Huh Why?!

Yellow = Happy

Green = Overwhelmed

Blue = Sad

Purple = Calm (very, very)

Brown = Board

Black = Ahhhhh

Pink = Calm, ~~Rady~~ Ready, OK

Now talk it out with a grown-up. What colors did you feel the most? What triggered different feelings? If you had some uncomfortable feelings, did you do anything to feel better? If you had some positive feelings, did you do anything to keep feeling good? What might you do tomorrow to solve a similar problem or work through a similar feeling?

Feelings Clouds

If you want to build emotional granularity—which involves understanding the feelings behind the feelings—you have to learn as many feelings words as possible. Feelings can be positive or negative, and sometimes they even feel like they're a little bit of both!

FEELINGS CLOUDS

Below are some words that describe positive emotions. Circle the ones you've felt before. Are there any other words you can add to this feelings cloud?

Positive Feelings Cloud

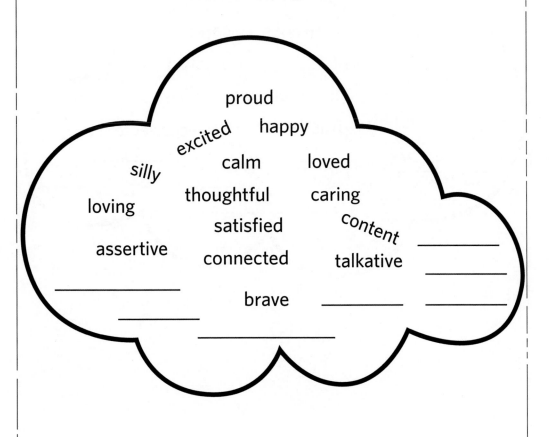

Now check out the feelings words that describe negative emotions. It's okay if you feel this way sometimes. Everyone does. No one is positive all of the time. Circle the feelings you've experienced before. Are there any other words you can add to this cloud?

Negative Feelings Cloud

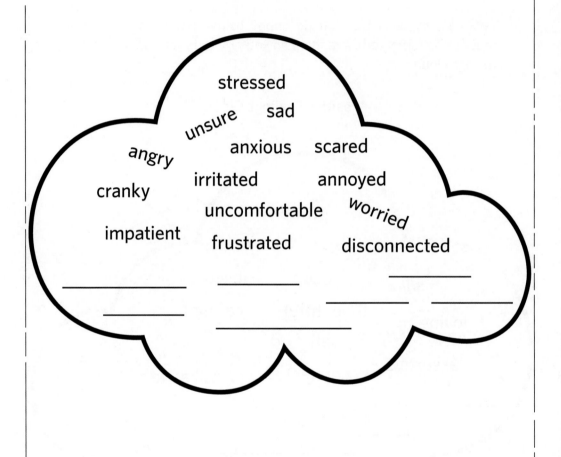

Worksheet

NAME THAT FEELING!

Now that you've added some new feelings words to your emotion vocabulary, let's try to figure out when you experience them. Close your eyes and take a few slow, deep breaths to clear your mind. When you open your eyes, read the first statement and fill in the answer that pops into your mind. Do the same with the other statements that follow.

When I wake up in the morning, I feel _____.

When I have to rush to get to school, I feel _____.

When I have extra time before school, I feel _____.

When I have to take a test, I feel _____.

When I forget my homework, I feel _____.

When I make a mistake, I feel _____.

When I help someone else, I feel _____.

When I play with my friends, I feel _____.

When I am left out, I feel _____.

When I can't fall asleep, I feel _____.

Add some of your own below:

When I _____, I feel _____.

When I _____, I feel _____.

When I _____, I feel _____.

When I _____, I feel _____.

When I _____, I feel _____.

(If you don't like writing, that's okay. You can say these out loud instead.)

PERSONIFY IT

When you give your stress a name and draw a picture of what it looks like, it's easier to talk back to it and to work through your uncomfortable emotions. I know that sounds a little silly, but it really does work.

In the square below, draw a picture of what you think your stress voice looks like. This is the voice inside your head that fills you with different worry thoughts. Dress it up and give it a personality! Once you've finished designing it, give it a name. Get to know it. You might add some thought bubbles to show some of the stress thoughts that run through your mind a lot.

Now that you know what your stress looks like, when you hear stress thoughts taking over your mind, imagine seeing your stress and talking back to it. You can say, "This is just my worry talking. I can handle this. You can't make me worry all day!"

Feelings Thermometer

All feelings have different levels. You might feel a little bit happy or really excited when something goes your way. You might be slightly worried about something or really, really stressed out. Use the picture on the next page to measure where you are on the feelings thermometer so you can figure out if you can cope on your own or if you need help.

FEELINGS THERMOMETER

Where are you on the feelings thermometer right now?

I feel: *Happy, but Anxios*

10
9   I need help!
8

7

6   I can to use my coping
5   skills to get through this.

4

3   I feel my temperature rising and
2   I'm thinking about what to do.
1

I'm doing well on my own!

Physical Stress Points

In the introduction, I talked about the different ways stress can affect you and what symptoms of stress might look like. A lot of kids have physical symptoms of stress. This happens when you experience big emotions and your body then sends out an alert for you to do something about those emotions. You might have a stomachache, a headache, or sore muscles. You might feel dizzy or have a fast heartbeat. These physical symptoms all represent different ways that emotions can be stored in your body. When you recognize your symptoms, you can work on coping.

Try to connect the dots between stress and your physical responses. Where do you feel stress in your body? Color the picture on the next page to show your physical stress points.

Worksheet

PHYSICAL STRESS POINTS

Where do you feel stress in your body?

back →

When was the last time you felt this way?

this morning/ yesterday
-I always feel this way

What helped you feel better?

-People complimenting m
-nothing

Create a Feelings Journal

Putting your feelings in writing can help you make sense of them. When you *personalize* a feelings journal, that means you make it your own. It becomes your special tool to work through the ups and downs of each day.

I've mentioned this before, but it's worth revisiting: You don't have to *love* writing to use a tool like this. Here are some other ways to use a journal that you might enjoy:

- Make a collage to get your feelings out by cutting and pasting pictures right into your journal.

- Doodle or draw your feelings.

- Keep it simple: Write about one up, one down, and one funny thing each day.

The best part is, you can revisit your journal whenever you need to. It helps to know that you've gotten through hard days before and can do it again.

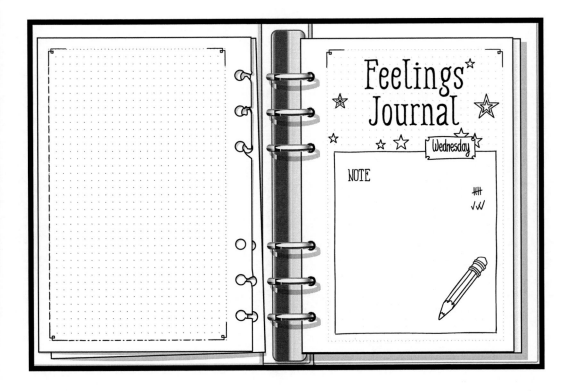

CHAPTER TWO

Building Distress Tolerance

Everyone has to learn how to handle the not-so-fun emotions, like sadness, anger, and stress. All kids, teens, and adults feel both positive and negative emotions every single day. The positive emotions are fun and feel good, but the negative ones can feel really bad sometimes. Learning how to cope with those feelings is called *building distress tolerance*.

It's super important to remember that emotions are usually temporary responses to stuff. When you feel really stressed, try to remember that it won't last forever. You will feel calm again. When you learn how to handle those pesky negative emotions, you won't feel as overwhelmed by them.

Stress Check-In

Now that you know a lot about feelings, it's time to focus on your stress and what causes it. To do so, it helps to do a little stress check-in at the end of each day. You can use the worksheet that's included or create your own.

Doing a daily stress check-in helps you evaluate your stress level and think about what increases and decreases your stress level. Both are equally important. When you know what kinds of triggers stress you out, you can learn to work through them. And when you figure out what makes you feel calm and happy during the day, you can try to find ways to do more of that.

Remember: Experiencing stress is just part of being human. We all have it. But you can learn to manage your stress so it doesn't overwhelm you. Like most other things you'll learn in life, the more you practice your coping skills, the easier they are to use when stress strikes.

You can make copies of the check-in sheet to keep handy or create a different system that works for you. Either way, a quick check-in gives you the time and space to think about your daily stress and how you handled it. Some days you might feel like your stress was no big deal and you handled it just fine, but other days you might feel like your stress was out of control. That's okay. You can always ask for help on the hard days. Helping each other out is what humans do best!

STRESS CHECK-IN

At the end of each day, use this sheet to think about what made you feel stressed during the day and how you managed it.

Where were you when you felt stressed?

☐ Home

☑ School

☑ Other: _volleyball_

What was happening?

A lot!!

_____

_____

How did you handle it?

Not very well

_____

_____

How BIG Is This Problem?

Have you ever noticed that stress can feel the same for problems of all different sizes? When our brains shift into stress-response mode, we tend to experience symptoms of stress before we even think through the situation. You might hear an adult refer to this as *overreacting*. Some adults even use the word *drama* to describe how kids react to difficult situations. But feeling stressed isn't the same as being dramatic, and until you learn how to cope with feelings of stress, it's difficult to avoid a big reaction. Here's a little secret: There's no perfect response to a stressful situation. You can only do your best on any given day.

One thing that can help you shift from stress-response mode to problem-solving mode a little bit faster is to do a problem intensity rating. Here's how it works:

1. Take a deep breath to release any uncomfortable or tight feelings in your body and slow your stress response.

2. Say out loud, "I'm having a problem. How big is this problem?"

3. Use the scale on the next page to rate how big your problem is. (Or you can just imagine the scale in your mind.) Is this problem a 5, and you can't figure out what to do? Or is it more of a 3, and you might be able to handle it on your own?

4. Pick a strategy and tackle the problem.

You might want to add your own strategies to the rating scale so you have choices on there that you know will work for you. It's always a good idea to make it your own.

HOW BIG IS THIS PROBLEM?

☆ ☆ ☆ ☆ ☆

★ ☆ ☆ ☆ ☆ 1. Not so big. I know what to do.

★ ★ ☆ ☆ ☆ 2. This feels stressful, but I'm brainstorming solutions.

★ ★ ★ ☆ ☆ 3. I'm stressed. I can do these things to calm down:

- Deep breathing

- _____

- _____

★ ★ ★ ★ ☆ 4. I feel overwhelmed. I can try these things:

- Coloring

- Jumping jacks

- _____

- _____

★ ★ ★ ★ ★ 5. I need adult help right away.

Catch That Feeling

When negative emotions (or yucky feelings, as I call them) enter your mind, it can be tempting to try to swat them away like you would an annoying fly. No one likes to have stressful or uncomfortable feelings. But the more you swat them away, the bigger they become in your mind. And the bigger the emotions feel, the more power they have over you.

Instead of swatting those feelings away, try catching them. Hold them in your catcher's glove and finish these sentences out loud:

I feel...

I feel this way because...

I will feel better when...

Sometimes feelings are just things we have to get through. It's okay to feel scared, stressed, mad, sad, or any other uncomfortable emotion. You can feel this way today and still have a good day tomorrow. That's how it is with stress. Learning to sit with discomfort actually helps you feel stronger and more confident in your ability to handle stressful situations.

Outside-Inside

Sometimes the emotions we show to the outside world don't match how we feel on the inside. A lot of kids feel like they should try to be happy and calm on the outside even if they're feeling stressed on the inside. If this describes you, you are definitely not alone.

On the first page of this activity, draw how you think you appear to other people when you're at school, playing a sport, or hanging out with friends. Do you look happy, silly, focused, or something else? Then, on the second page, fill in the clouds to describe how you sometimes feel on the inside in these situations. This can be a mix of positive and negative emotions. Fill in as many emotions as you can think of.

When you're done, answer these questions:

- Why do you think you keep some of these emotions hidden?

- Is there someone you can share them with?

- What might happen when you start sharing your inside feelings?

OUTSIDE-INSIDE

The feelings we show on the outside don't always match how we feel on the inside.

On the outside I look like I feel this way...

Inside my mind I feel this way...

In these clouds, write down all the thoughts and feelings you are having. These can be happy thoughts, sad thoughts, worried thoughts, excited thoughts—any thoughts!

Three Easy Breathing Techniques

If you hear grown-ups talk about the importance of deep breathing, that's because it's your best defense against feeling stressed, anxious, or even angry. When you take a good, deep breath, you can actually calm down your nervous system. (You might remember from an earlier chapter that the nervous system is in charge of sending your body into fight-or-flight mode in response to stress.) That's right. Deep breathing changes your whole response to stress. The problem is that most people don't know how to do it the right way.

Counting in your head as you take your breaths makes a big difference. Here's how it works:

- Breathe in for a count of four.

- Hold for a count of four.

- Breathe out for a count of four.

- Hold for a count of four.

Repeat this process three times and you'll feel *a lot* better. If that sounds boring, keep reading to see three deep-breathing strategies that make breathing a little more fun.

SQUARE BREATHING

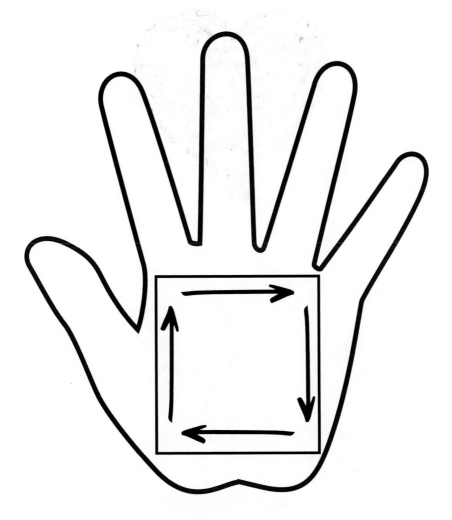

**Trace a square in the palm of your hand
while you do your counts.**

BALLOON BREATHING

"Every day above ground is a great day" (Pitbull)

- Choose a color for your imaginary balloon.

- Add a design.

- Use your counts while you inflate your balloon.

- Tie it with a string.

- Write a positive thought on it.

- Let it fly away to someone you care about.

RAINBOW BREATHING

1. While you do your counts and breathe, think of all of your favorite red things and color in the first stripe on the rainbow with a red marker or crayon.

2. Next, move to the orange stripe and repeat.

3. Continue until you breathe through the whole rainbow!

Take 5 to Calm Down!

Now that you know your early warning signs of stress and worry, you can pay attention to how your body feels during stressful situations. When you feel your symptoms coming on, it's a good time to Take 5.

This is a pretty easy strategy that reminds you to take deep, calming breaths while you think of positive things in your life that make you feel calm. These positive things can be anything that brings you a sense of joy or a feeling of peace. There are no right or wrong answers when you Take 5. As you take deep breaths with this exercise, remember to count to four with each breath in and out.

TAKE 5 TO CALM DOWN

5 Take 5 deep breaths.

4 Name 4 people who care about you.

3 Name 3 things that make you smile.

2 Take 2 more deep breaths.

1 Share 1 happy memory.

Hit the Pause Button in Your Brain

Did you know you have a pause button in your brain? Okay, not *literally* a button, but you can pause your stress thoughts by using grounding techniques. *Grounding* a fancy way of saying you can cope with overwhelming feelings by focusing your attention on what is happening around you right now.

And here's the good news about grounding techniques: You can do them anywhere, at any time, and no one will even know you're doing them! They are simple, effective, and sneaky. So if you feel super stressed in the middle of a class at school, you can work through it right at your desk by using these techniques.

There are different kinds of grounding techniques. Some techniques use your imagination to help you interrupt your stress thoughts by having you check in with your five senses: your sense of sight, sound, smell, hearing, and taste. Other techniques ask you to shift your thinking or focus your thoughts on something else. There are also more physical techniques that help you pay attention to what's happening right in front of you.

All these techniques help you work through stress and anxiety by calming your nervous system. Try a few and see which ones work for you.

Grounding with Your Imagination

Close your eyes and count out your breaths. While you're breathing, imagine the following things:

- Your favorite place (What can you see, smell, feel, taste, and hear?)

- Your favorite food (What does it look like? How does it feel? What does it taste and smell like?)

- Your favorite comfort object (Is it soft, fuzzy, or squishy? What does it look and feel like?)

Grounding with Physical Sensations

These quick physical actions can help you focus (or refocus) your attention on what is happening *right now*.

- Hold an ice cube to your wrists or the back of your neck.

- Drink cold water.

- Rub a smooth stone in your hand.

- Squeeze a stress ball.

- Do ten jumping jacks.

- Clap your hands ten times loud and ten times soft.

- Rub your hands together for ten seconds.

- Stretch your arms behind your back.

- Jog in place for thirty seconds.

Grounding with Your Thoughts

Try these tips to make your thinking work for you.

- Say what you see: Name five things you can see.

- Narrate your experience: What's happening? Say it out loud.

- List the people who care about you.

- Sing a song that makes you feel good.

Choose Your Path

Part of building distress tolerance is learning to make important decisions during high-stress moments. This isn't easy to do. When your brain shifts into fight-or-flight mode, or when you feel overwhelmed with anxiety, it can be difficult to make quick decisions that help you cope.

To get you through these situations, it helps to think ahead. You can make a plan in advance by thinking about what coping strategies will work in different situations. Then if that difficult situation comes up in the future, you'll already know which path to choose that keeps you moving forward!

To create this plan, look at the two paths shown on the following worksheet. One path is called Coping Lane. On this path, list the coping strategies you've learned so far that you think will work for you. The other path is called Helper Street. On this path, list all the people who can help you get through a tough situation. Fill out both paths and revisit this page often to add more skills and helpers to your list.

CHOOSE YOUR PATH!

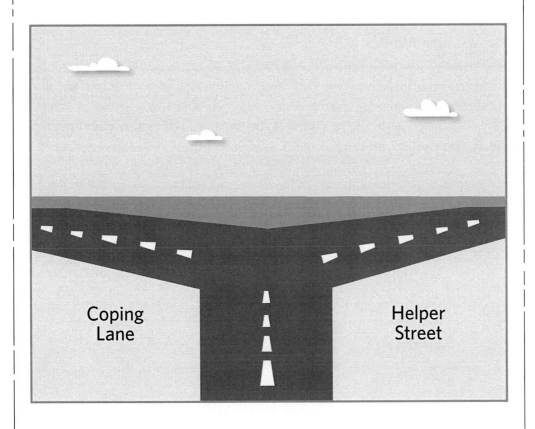

Coping Lane

Helper Street

Use Your Words!

Parents often say "Use your words!" when kids are little and first learning to talk, but it's usually lost on them. It's actually a skill that becomes even more important for older kids. That's because when you're under stress, using positive words, phrases, and even songs can help you feel calm and in control. Let's practice using your words by creating a catchy mantra and singing your stress.

Create a Catchy Mantra

Mantras are short phrases we can repeat to ourselves to remind us of our strengths. These come in handy when you first feel those signs of stress or anxiety. Whenever you notice yourself feeling stressed, repeat your mantra to remind yourself that you can handle it. Use one of these or create your own:

- I can do hard things.

- Stress is temporary.

- I know I can handle this.

- _____

- _____

- _____

Sing Your Stress

It might sound silly, but another way to take some control over a stressful situation is to change the lyrics to your favorite song so that the song is about your stress. It also adds a little humor, which can calm your body and mind when you're overwhelmed. So go ahead and rewrite your favorite songs so you know the words to sing when the going gets tough!

Fly Away Feelings

Sometimes the best way to get through stressful feelings is to label them, write them down, and fly them away. Negative emotions often feel like they control you when you aren't sure what to do with them, but by noticing your emotions and dealing with them as they arise, you gain control.

The next time you feel overwhelmed with distress, shout out what you're feeling, write it down on a piece of paper, and then fold it into a paper airplane and send that negative emotion soaring away from you.

FLY AWAY FEELINGS

Step 1: Write/draw feelings & triggers of feelings

How are you feeling? What things caused those feelings?

Step 2: Fold the paper airplane

Creating the airplane gives you time to work through your feelings.

Step 3: Repeat the feelings out loud and send the airplane on a trip!

Talk about your feelings with a grown-up you trust.

Step 4: Chase the airplane and repeat or make a new one

Learn that feelings don't just disappear but you can learn to cope with them.

Progressive Muscle Relaxation

When you're feeling stressed, you're probably holding a lot of tension—or the feeling of tightness or pressure—in all of your muscles. That's really common. We do this without even realizing it. You might notice you clench your fists or jaw when you're stressed. Or you might tense your arm and leg muscles. You might even have neck, shoulder, or back pain. All of that can happen from muscle tension.

Progressive muscle relaxation (PMR) is a strategy that helps you release that tension stored up in your muscles—one muscle group at a time—until you get it all out of your body. When you let the stress out, you feel a little more relaxed. One great thing about this strategy is that you can do it anywhere, even at your desk or during a long a car ride. Follow the steps on the next page to give it a try!

PROGRESSIVE MUSCLE RELAXATION

Clench and hold your fist and arm muscles for a count of four, then slowly release for a count of four. Repeat.

Clench and hold your feet and leg muscles for a count of four, then slowly release for a count of four. Repeat.

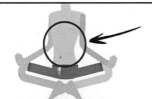

Clench and hold your stomach muscles for a count of four, then slowly release for a count of four. Repeat.

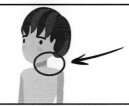

Clench and hold your shoulder and neck muscles for a count of four, then slowly release for a count of four. Repeat.

Clench and hold your face muscles for a count of four, then slowly release for a count of four. Repeat.

Stress Coping Kit

Everyone needs a stress coping kit. One fun way to do this is to write down a bunch of different coping strategies on popsicle sticks and to keep them in a jar. When you're stressed and need a strategy, pull out a stick and try that strategy out. You can also write them on sticky notes and keep them in a box. It doesn't really matter where you keep your strategies; it just helps to have them written down.

It's a good idea to have different strategies for different moods and situations. Sometimes you might want a quiet activity to calm down, but other times you might want a more physical activity to release some tension. Here are some examples. What will you put in your kit?

Calming Strategies

Listen to music

Color, draw, or paint

Trace a pattern

Use Play-Doh®

Do a crossword puzzle

Physical Strategies

Do ten push-ups

Go for a walk or run

Ride your bike

Dance

Stretch

Solo Activities

Journal

Read

Write a story

Cuddle a pet

Do deep breathing

Squeeze a stress ball

Family/Group Activities

Play a game

Bake or cook something

Read aloud

Do an obstacle course

Go on a nature walk

CHAPTER THREE

Overcoming Obstacles

Stress happens. At every age and every stage, people encounter stress. When kids experience stress and worry, they have difficulty seeing their way through obstacles. Stress can make even a small problem feel like a huge challenge that can't be solved. The good news is that you can learn to work through your stress and overcome your obstacles. By changing your thinking, you can actually change your outcomes.

With that good news comes some work on your part. Learning to overcome obstacles is all about believing in your ability to solve problems. YOU can make it happen, but you have to learn to trust yourself.

Have you ever heard a teacher talk about "thinking outside the box"? That's a teacher's way of saying that we sometimes need to be creative with our problem-solving skills. We have to take what we know and add new ideas to it. So instead of sticking with the same strategy over and over, you learn to take a look at the problem from a different point of view and try something new.

Thinking outside the box helps a ton when it comes to overcoming obstacles. A lot of times, adults give kids the strategies they need to do hard things, but when you get into the habit of solving your own problems, you'll be amazed at the great ideas you have!

Zones of Control

The first step to figuring out how to solve a problem is to think about what's in your control and what's not. Your stress response might try to tell you that you have NO control over the problem, but that's just stress talking. Don't believe everything your brain tells you when you're trying to cope with something hard.

You can talk through what's happening and figure out what to do by separating your problem into two different zones: the Zone of Control and the Zone of No Control. Here's how to do it, step by step:

1. First, state the problem. This is whatever is bothering you or stressing you out.

2. Then state your goal. This is whatever you'd like to happen.

3. Next, identify all the pieces that contribute to the problem.

4. Sort all these pieces into the appropriate zones using the circle in the worksheet.

5. Anything in the Zone of No Control won't help you right now. Leave those alone.

6. Now look at the pieces you placed in the Zone of Control. Identify how you can use these to solve your problem.

Let's try an example before you get started. Imagine that you get into an argument with your friends because you want to play Four Square, but they insist on Capture the Flag… again. There are three of them and one of you. You feel like they never listen to your ideas, so you become frustrated and refuse to play. They tease you and tell you not to act like a "baby" before going off to play without you. On the next page, you'll find an example of how using the zones can help you solve this problem.

ZONES OF CONTROL

Problem: My friends won't listen to my ideas for games.

Goal: I want to talk to my friends about switching up games.

Making plans for recess

How I react

My choice to play with other kids

Whether I'm positive about new things

Zone of Control

Zone of NO Control

How my friends react to me

What my friends choose to do

When I get outvoted

How my friends feel about new games

Solution: I can ask my friends what they think about making a schedule where we take turns playing a few different games during recess. I can also try playing with a new friend group to have more choices.

Your turn!

ZONES OF CONTROL

Problem: _____

Goal: _____

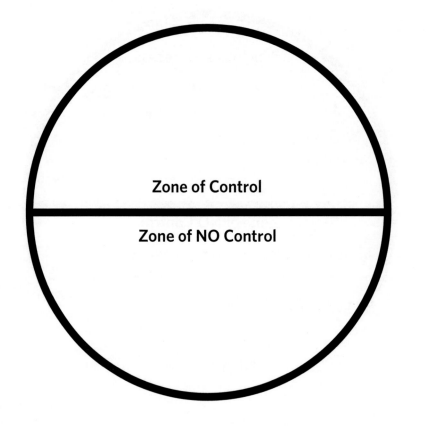

Zone of Control

Zone of NO Control

Solution: _____

_____

_____

_____

Take Charge!

A lot of kids don't know what to do when they encounter an unexpected obstacle. Remember when we talked about fight-or-flight mode? When you feel like you want to run away and hide from something difficult, your brain is in flight mode. And when you feel like you want to scream and yell in response to these same problems, your brain is in fight mode.

Sometimes the solution to a problem is fairly simple. For instance, if your friends are arguing about what game to play, you can create a schedule to take turns. But sometimes it's hard to see a solution right away. That's okay. You're not expected to have all the answers right away. No one does!

One thing you can do is brainstorm. When you change your thinking from "I don't know how to do this" to "I wonder if any of these ideas will help," you move out of fight-or-flight mode and back into problem-solving mode. The key to a good brainstorm is to remember that *all* ideas are worth considering. Write down every idea that comes to mind (even the super funny ones!). You can evaluate whether or not you want to use that idea later.

There are two ways that brainstorming helps: It gets you unstuck so you can move forward in a healthy way, and it helps you find a reasonable solution to deal with the obstacle. Brainstorming helps you take charge of the situation!

I love to brainstorm on a whiteboard because it's easy to add and erase ideas, but you can use the box on the next page. Follow these steps:

1. Write down every possible solution you can think of. Ask a friend or adult to help if you have trouble getting started. Sometimes one idea leads to another.

2. Step back and sort the ideas. Do any of them overlap? Group them together on the board.

3. Evaluate your ideas. Think about which ones might work and which ones might not be all that helpful. Erase or cross out the ones that aren't doable.

4. Circle your top three. Pick one and give it a try!

TAKE CHARGE!

Problem: _____

Brainstorm it:

Top three:

1. _____

2. _____

3. _____

I'll try this solution first: _____

If I need help, I can ask: _____

Relaxing Stories

A lot of kids struggle with sleep when they are stressed. In fact, sleep troubles are generally a clue that kids are feeling stressed or anxious. When you finally stop moving and doing things, the stress you've pushed down all day takes center stage. This can trigger insomnia, which is a fancy way of saying you can't fall asleep at night.

One way to decrease stress at night is to use the power of your imagination to create a relaxing story that helps you fall asleep. It's like having a calming movie play in your mind as you drift off to sleep. It's best to create this story ahead of time—ideally during a calm daytime moment—so you won't have to come up with it at night!

To create your relaxing story, close your eyes and picture a calming environment that makes you feel happy. You can think about an experience you've had or a place you've actually been to, or you can just make one up in your mind. Try to imagine as many details as you can about this place. What do you see around you? What sounds and smells do you notice? Is there anyone with you? What are you doing in this happy place? Try to imagine the scene in as much detail as you can.

Then open your eyes and use the boxes on the next page to fill in your movie reel, frame by frame. Add as many details as possible to each box. Tonight, when you're trying to fall asleep, close your eyes and picture each frame of your relaxing story, as if each scene is playing on a movie screen in your mind.

You can also make a recording of your relaxing story so you can play it each night at bedtime. Remember to describe all the details and to use your best calming voice. This becomes your own sleep story that you can tell yourself when you're trying to fall asleep at night!

Worksheet

RELAXING STORY

Fill in your movie reel, frame by frame. Remember to add lots of details!

When you're done, make a recording to listen to at night!

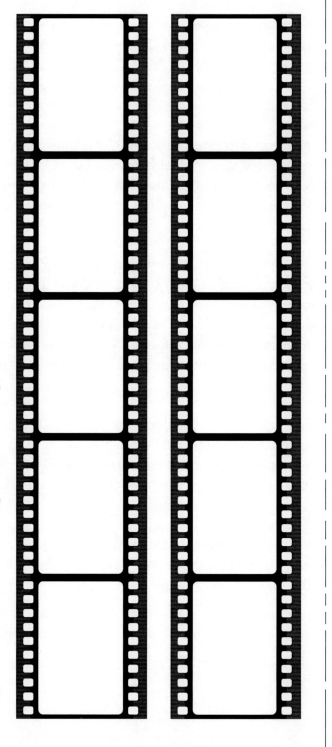

This or That?

When you have a hard time deciding how to deal with a situation that makes you feel stressed, it can help to make two lists of actions you could take: your gut reaction (or your first instinct) and your alternatives.

Sometimes your gut reaction will be the best response, but other times you might need an alternative. For example, you can use some solutions at home, but not at school. That's why choices are important. You always need more than one strategy. Check out this example:

Obstacle: The other kids are talking about weekend plans at lunch, but you're not included.

THIS (gut reaction)

Get up and leave the table

Tell on them for excluding you

Join a different group at recess

THAT (alternative)

Get more information

Tell them how you feel

Work through it with a teacher

Your turn!

THIS OR THAT?

Obstacle: _____

THIS (gut reaction)

THAT (alternative)

_____	_____
_____	_____
_____	_____
_____	_____
_____	_____
_____	_____
_____	_____
_____	_____
_____	_____
_____	_____
_____	_____

Circle the ones you want to try.

Worry Brain/Calm Brain

We all have a part of our brain that thinks calm thoughts and a part of our brain that thinks worry thoughts. That's natural. And sometimes our worry brains are really helpful! They remind us to look twice before crossing the street. The problem is that the worry brain can become too active and loud, which makes it difficult for the calm brain to do its job. It's really important to find a balance between the two.

For this activity, use the Calm Brain sheet to fill in all the calm, hopeful, and happy thoughts that run through your brain. On the Worry Brain sheet, fill in all the worry thoughts that your worry brain sends throughout the day. Now look at the two sheets side by side. How do those worry thoughts make you feel? What about the calm ones? How can you use your calm thoughts to work through your worry ones? Are there any that seem to go together?

When your worry brain and your calm brain work together, you're better able to solve problems and sit with uncomfortable emotions. To get these two parts of your brain working together, one helpful trick is to finish this sentence: "I feel worried about (*say worry here*) right now, but this is temporary. I will feel (*say positive emotion here*) when I do (*say action to decrease worry here*)."

Example:

I feel worried about <u>my spelling test</u> right now, but this is temporary.

I will feel <u>happy</u> when I <u>get out to recess and run around with my friends</u>.

Your turn! Pick one of the worries you wrote down on the Worry Brain sheet and see how one of the calm thoughts can help you manage the situation.

I feel worried about _____ right now, but this is temporary.

I will feel _____ when I _____.

CALM BRAIN

Fill in all the calm, hopeful, and happy thoughts that run through your brain throughout the day.

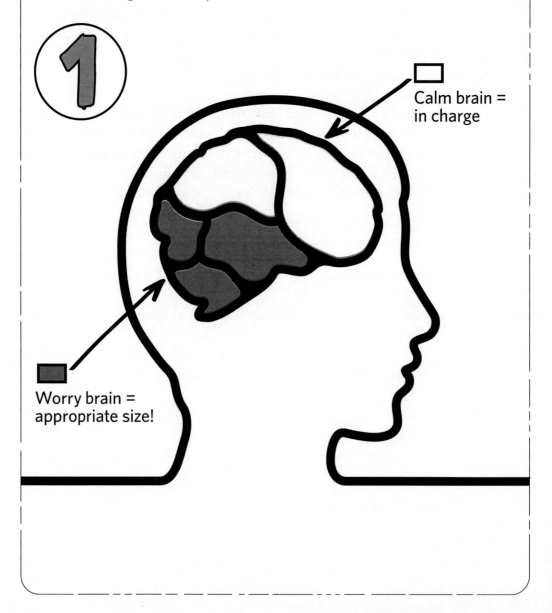

Calm brain = in charge

Worry brain = appropriate size!

WORRY BRAIN

Fill in all the worry thoughts that your worry brain sends throughout the day.

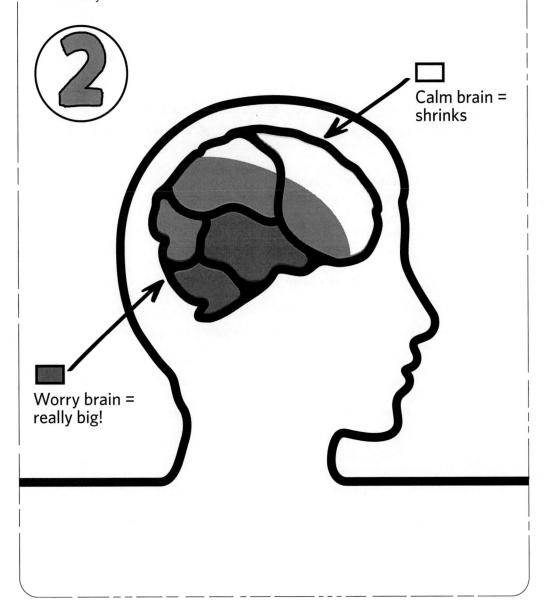

Calm brain = shrinks

Worry brain = really big!

Problem-Solver Cards

One of the hardest parts of overcoming obstacles is trying to think of the best problem-solving strategy to use. These handy problem-solver cards give you the steps you need to figure out how big the problem is, to come up with a plan, and to put the plan into action.

When you learn to work through a problem by following specific steps, it actually gives you time to slow down your stress response and think clearly. Here are the five steps involved in problem solving:

1. **State the problem.** This might sound simple, but sometimes we get so caught up in how we *feel* about a problem that it's hard to figure out what the problem is. Take three deep breaths and state the problem out loud.

2. **Identify the barriers.** Barriers are things that make it hard to solve a problem. Saying them out loud helps alert your brain to think through them.

3. **Develop a plan.** Now that you know the problem and the barriers, what *can* you do to work around them?

4. **Test the plan.** Give it a try! Your first plan might need work, but you'll only know that if you try it out.

5. **Think about the results.** Did your plan work? If not, what needs changing? Keep working on it and try again.

Example: You and your friends can't get a game going at recess because everyone is arguing.

1. **Problem**: Fighting over what game to play makes it impossible to play.

2. **Barriers**: Kids are arguing and all have their own ideas.

3. **Plan**: Everyone puts their idea on a piece of paper, and we pick from a hat.

4. **Test**: It takes ten minutes to find paper and write our ideas down.

5. **Assess**: Good idea, but maybe Rock, Paper, Scissors would be faster.

On the next page, you'll find some problem-solving cards to remind you of each of these five steps. Cut these cards out and keep them within reach, or design your own!

PROBLEM-SOLVER CARDS

1

State the problem.

2

Name the barriers.

3

Develop a plan.

4

Test the plan.

5

Assess the results.

Mountain Climber

A lot of kids feel like they have huge mountains to climb when they encounter obstacles. And each time something sets them back on their climb, it feels like they'll never reach their goal of getting to the top. The trick about climbing mountains, though, is to climb one section at a time and to take breaks. You can't race to the top; you have to pace yourself.

Imagine you are climbing a mountain of obstacles. Think about where you need to begin. You can't start halfway up the mountain. You have to start at the beginning and take small steps. If you encounter a slippery rock or an overgrown trail, you have to stop and think about how to work around it.

Fill in the stops along this mountain trail to outline how you can overcome a problem. First, identify your struggle at the bottom of the mountain. That's your starting point. Next, think of one small step you can take to work through it. That's your first water break. Plan out at least three steps before you reach the top. Congrats! You just figured out how to overcome your obstacle.

MOUNTAIN CLIMBER

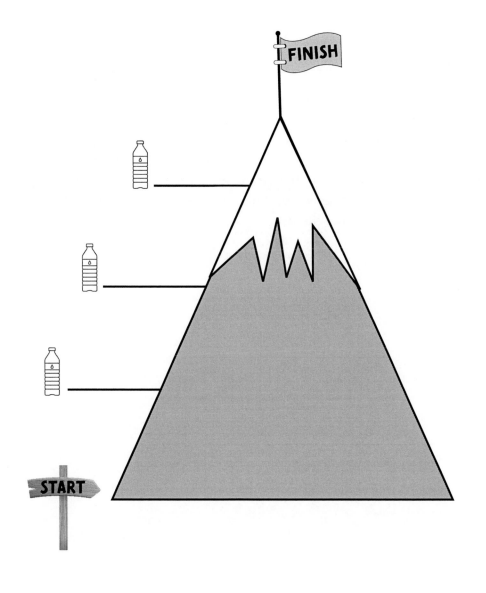

Healthy/Unhealthy Ways of Coping

A lot of kids feel mad, frustrated, or overwhelmed when unexpected obstacles get in the way of accomplishing goals. When kids feel a rush of negative emotions, they tend to either externalize them (let them out by doing things like yelling, stomping their feet, or slamming doors) or internalize them (keep them in, which causes the emotions to build up and feel bigger and bigger). These are both examples of unhealthy ways of coping.

Healthy coping skills help you get your feelings out without hurting anyone else in the process. They allow you to work through your emotions so you're ready to solve the problem. In contrast, unhealthy coping skills end up making you (and the people around you) feel worse.

On the next page are some examples of healthy and unhealthy coping strategies. It's okay if you've used some of the unhealthy ones in the past. That's why you're learning new ones now! Circle the strategies from either category that you've already used. Put a star by new ones you might want to try. If you can think of other strategies, add them to the list.

HEALTHY/UNHEALTHY WAYS OF COPING

Healthy
- Deep breathing
- Taking a walk
- Using "I feel" statements
- Playing with a pet
- Closing my eyes and counting to ten
- Writing down my feelings

Unhealthy
- Yelling
- Blaming others
- Stomping away
- Arguing
- Shutting down and ignoring everyone
- Keeping my feelings inside

_____

_____

_____

_____

_____

_____

_____

Obstacle Pyramid

When you're feeling upset or overwhelmed, even a small obstacle (like when you can't find your math book before school) can feel big. That can happen because your brain shifts into fight-or-flight mode whenever you encounter an obstacle, or it might also happen because you're already stressed, and a new obstacle feels like *one more thing* that's hard to handle. It could also be that you haven't had a lot of experience overcoming obstacles on your own, so you don't have the confidence you need to take control of the situation.

The good news is that most obstacles aren't as big as we think they are in the heat of the moment. When we are able to calm down and think logically, we can usually find a way to overcome the obstacle.

Use the obstacle pyramid on the next page to evaluate how big your obstacle actually is and to see what you can do to work through an obstacle of any size. Next to each different obstacle level, write some strategies you can use or people you can ask for help. That's an important step. Knowing what to do or whom to turn to for help gives you an action plan for future obstacles.

OBSTACLE PYRAMID

No big deal! — I can handle this alone.

Bump — I can handle this alone by doing this: _____

Medium obstacle — I can make this change: _____

Big obstacle — I need support from: _____

Huge obstacle — I need help from: _____

Size of my obstacle: _____

Strategy to solve: _____

Who can help?: _____

Graphic Short Story

Graphic novels are fun to read because you can see the story play out in words and pictures. You can also pinpoint exactly where a problem occurs and what a character might need to do to resolve it.

You can do the same thing by creating your own graphic short story. Think of a problem you didn't handle as well as you had hoped. How did it start? How did you feel once you realized you were in the middle of a problem you didn't know how to solve? What choices did you make in the moment? Break the scenario down, scene by scene. If you like to draw, great! If you don't, you can use words, doodle, or even collage your story.

Once your story is complete, take a look at it to find the place where you could have used a better problem-solving strategy. Circle that box in the graphic short story. What was happening in that box? What strategies might you use the next time? Write those down near that box as a reminder.

You won't always use the best possible strategies in the heat of the moment. Sometimes emotions take over and it's difficult to remember your new skills. Using a graphic short story to work through it later helps you learn something from the incident and think about what you'll do the next time you experience something similar. That's important work that helps you build your skills.

GRAPHIC SHORT STORY

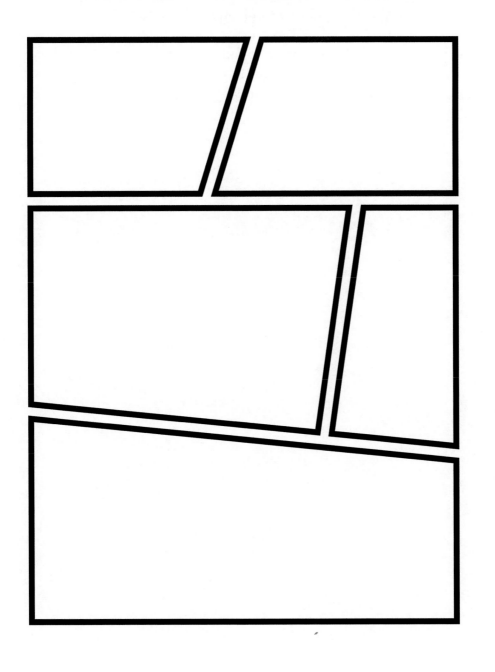

Use the Stoplight!

You will encounter obstacles every single day. Some of them will be really big, but many of them will be fairly small. All of them require you to think before you act. Slowing down to consider the situation first helps you make positive decisions. One way to slow down and take the best steps to overcome your obstacle is to imagine that there's a stoplight in your mind.

Use the worksheet on the next page to follow the stoplight from red to green. When you're done, think about how it went. Did your plan work? If yes, congratulations! If no, that's okay. You can go back to the red light and begin again.

USE THE STOPLIGHT!

STOP: TAKE THREE DEEP BREATHS.

What is the obstacle?: _____

_____

SLOW: THINK ABOUT YOUR PLAN.

1st idea: _____

2nd idea: _____

GO! USE YOUR PLAN.

What do you hope will happen? _____

_____

Weigh Your Options

There are usually positives and negatives to any solution for a problem. These are called *pros* and *cons*. For example, if you're arguing with a peer about what game what to play, an easy solution is to take turns. The pro (the positive) is that you stop arguing because you have a plan. The con (the negative), however, is that you might have to wait a while for your turn.

When you weigh the pros and cons of a solution *before* you choose what to do, it gives you time to think about the best choice for the scenario. When you're looking at pros and cons, you can imagine that you're filling one side of a scale with pros and the other with cons. Which side has more? That will help you guide your decision-making.

WEIGH YOUR OPTIONS

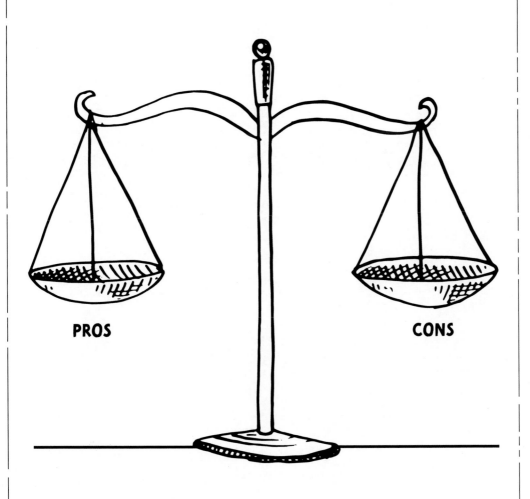

PROS   CONS

Preparing for Setbacks

Even when you feel like you have problem solving mastered, you can still experience setbacks. It's natural to freeze up and forget your skills sometimes. That even happens to adults! So it helps to plan ahead for potential setbacks.

The more time you spend thinking about how to overcome your obstacles, the more your brain internalizes these problem-solving skills. *Internalize* just means that your brain learns how to use these skills without even thinking twice about it. Pretty soon, you'll be solving problems all day long like a pro! Fill out the following worksheet to have a setback plan in place.

PREPARING FOR SETBACKS

My three favorite problem-solving strategies:

1. _____

2. _____

3. _____

These work for me because: _____

_____

Three people I can turn to if I need help:

1. _____

2. _____

3. _____

If my plan doesn't work the first time, I can try this instead:

_____

_____

_____

CHAPTER FOUR

Building Communication Skills

Believe it or not, it's important to practice good communication when working through stress. *Communication* is just a big word that means you can talk about things with other people and share what you are thinking and feeling. When kids are able to communicate their needs with confidence, they are better able to ask for help, to express their feelings, and to stand up for themselves and others. Good communication is especially important in helping you manage hard situations that can trigger stress, like having a conflict with a peer or dealing with a bully.

What makes for good communication? Good communication involves being *assertive*, which means you stand up for yourself with a calm and confident voice. This is in contrast to an *aggressive* communication style (which involves being rude, bossy, or mean) and a *passive* communication style (which involves not standing up for yourself and pretending that everything is okay—even when it's not).

It takes time to build assertive communication skills, and sometimes kids get these three communication styles mixed up. If you don't know the differences between them yet, don't worry. You'll learn all about communication in this chapter.

Here are descriptions of these different communication styles. As you read through each description, think about how *you* communicate with others. Hint: You might use different communication styles at different times.

Passive Communication:

- Difficulty making eye contact

- Saying "I don't know" or "I'm not sure" a lot

- Not speaking what's on your mind

- Speaking in a quiet voice

- Apologizing frequently

- Not wanting to speak in groups

- Having a slumped body position

Aggressive Communication:

- Interrupting or talking over other people

- Dominating conversations

- Talking in a loud, rude, or mean voice

- Using threatening or intimidating body language

- Using put-downs

- Blaming others

- Getting into frequent arguments

Assertive Communication:

- Making good eye contact or looking near the other person

- Using a calm, clear, and firm voice

- Saying no without feeling guilty

- Nodding and asking follow-up questions to show you're listening

- Sharing your concerns with confidence

- Standing tall, with welcoming body positioning

Next, you'll take an assessment to figure out what your communication style is. This will help you figure out what skills you want to work on.

Worksheet

WHAT'S MY STYLE?

Think about how you communicate with your friends, siblings, parents, teachers, and other people in your life. As you work through these lists, put a check mark by any statement that you think applies to you. It doesn't matter if there are a few from each list!

Style A

☐ I tend to look at the ground when I'm talking to someone and have trouble making eye contact.

☐ I say "I'm not sure" or "I don't know" a lot when people ask my opinion.

☐ I speak quietly when I do answer questions.

☐ I have a hard time speaking in groups.

☐ I usually let my friends or other people in the group make decisions.

☐ When I answer questions, I often begin with "I'm not sure if this is right, but..." or "I might be wrong, but..."

☐ I find it hard to talk if it feels like people are staring at me.

☐ I apologize even if I didn't do anything wrong.

Style B

☐ I talk fast and use a loud voice.

☐ I'm usually the most talkative person in a group of people.

☐ I sometimes get really close to people to make sure they're paying attention.

☐ I get into arguments when I think something isn't fair to me.

- ☐ I am sarcastic sometimes.
- ☐ I make jokes that others might not think are funny when I'm making a point.
- ☐ I don't let people finish talking if I have something important to say.
- ☐ I like other people to know I'm right.

Style C

- ☐ I feel confident when I speak.
- ☐ I try my best to make eye contact.
- ☐ I feel calm when I speak.
- ☐ My voice is clear and easy to hear.
- ☐ I can project my voice to the group.
- ☐ I show I'm listening by nodding my head and asking questions.
- ☐ I wait for people to finish before I start talking.
- ☐ I feel comfortable saying no when I need to.

Now count up all the phrases you checked off. Which category had the most?

- **"A" category:** You tend to be a little passive and have trouble speaking up. You don't always express your needs. You can learn to assert yourself.

- **"B" category:** You tend to be an aggressive communicator. You might need help with listening skills or learning to slide in and out of conversations.

- **"C" category:** It sounds like you're already practicing assertive communication. Keep working on your listening skills and expressing your ideas and needs with peers and adults.

Mirror It!

Sometimes it can be hard to know how you communicate because you don't actually see yourself talking! You might think you're standing tall and making eye contact, but another person might think you appear distracted or bored.

A great way to work on your assertive communication skills is to practice in the mirror. That way you can see your *nonverbal cues*, which have to do with the body language, facial expressions, and tone of voice you use when speaking. Some examples of assertive nonverbal cues are smiling, using a confident voice, and making good eye contact. Good communication isn't just about *what* you say, but also *how* you say it. That's why paying attention to your nonverbal cues is so important.

To practice your nonverbal communication skills, stand in front of a mirror and tell yourself a story. Make eye contact with yourself, smile when something is funny, and respond when there's a pause. It might sound silly to talk to yourself, but it actually helps build your confidence with speaking.

Draw yourself speaking with confidence in the mirror on the next page. What nonverbal cues show others that you are confident?

MIRROR IT!

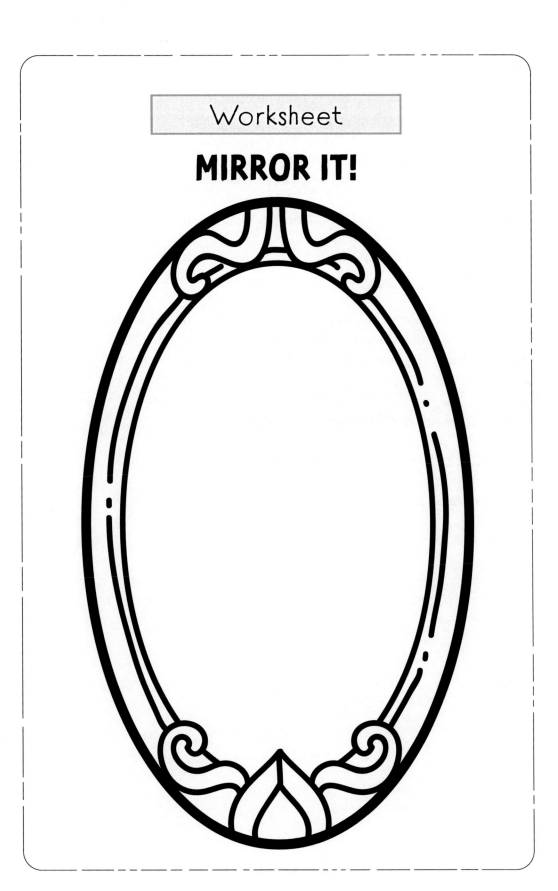

I Statements

It's helpful to get into the habit of using "I statements" when you assert your feelings, thoughts, and needs. When you do this, you avoid blaming other people for things or accusing them of causing your feelings. Owning your feelings is powerful, and it helps you focus on what you need to do to feel better.

Doing this can take some practice. Here's how "I statements" work:

I feel (*say your feeling here*) when (*say what causes this feeling*) because (*explain why*). Please (*state what you want the other person to do differently*).

Let's try an example so you can see how it works. Pretend a friend is arguing with you about something that happened at soccer practice, and your friend's voice is getting very loud and intimidating. Here's an "I statement" you could use:

I feel <u>uncomfortable</u> when <u>we argue about soccer</u>

because <u>I'm not sure how to handle it</u>.

Please <u>give me a chance to talk</u>.

Your turn!

I STATEMENTS

Think of a couple different scenarios when you needed to assert yourself but weren't sure how, and fill in the blanks to describe how you could have responded in a more assertive way.

I feel _____ when _____

because _____.

Please _____.

I feel _____ when _____

because _____.

Please _____.

I feel _____ when _____

because _____.

Please _____.

Boundaries Manifesto

Learning to say no and to set healthy boundaries for yourself takes practice. A *boundary* is something that sets limits on your personal space and that defines what you are and are not comfortable with. Boundaries can be physical (like wanting to keep your body private) and emotional (like treating others with kindness and expecting them to do the same in return).

A good first step in creating healthy boundaries is to craft your own boundaries manifesto. This is a statement about your personal needs. It will help you remember that you have the right to stand up for yourself, get help when you need it, and say, "No!"

Fill in the manifesto on the next page with your own statements about being assertive. You might include things like "I have the right to disagree in a respectful way," "I have the right to say no," and "I have the right to feel angry."

What boundaries can you set that will help you feel confident, heard, and understood? Thinking about these things is an important first step. Once you have them written down, you can begin practicing by sharing them with your grown-ups.

BOUNDARIES MANIFESTO

I have the right to ...

What Do They Think?

"What did you say?" Have you ever had someone say this to you because they misunderstood you? Sometimes we think we're being clear and assertive, when in reality, other people have trouble understanding us. That's because everyone is different, and we all have our own responses and communication styles. If you've ever had a conversation where someone didn't understand what you were saying, that's okay. It's an opportunity to think about the words you used and to try again.

Fill out the thought bubbles on the next page to work through some confusing conversations you've had. What did you mean to say to the other person? What did that person think you said? How can you adjust for next time? When you consider the other person's point of view, it is called *perspective taking*, and it helps you think about how you communicate with others and how they feel as a result. When you do this, you give yourself a chance to work on your communication skills.

WHAT DO THEY THINK?

I said...	They heard...	Next time...

WORD SHIFT

When we're stressed or upset, it's easy to blame others or to say things we later regret. That's because when we're stressed, we don't always stop and think about the words we use. This can hurt other people, even when we don't mean to.

One thing you can do to avoid this is to practice making simple changes to your language so you don't blame others for your feelings. You can assert yourself and get your point across in a calm way that helps others understand your point of view. Check out the examples below:

Instead of:
You're wrong!
You upset me!
You don't pay attention to me!

Try this:
I disagree.
I feel upset.
I feel lonely.

Your turn! Think of some phrases you can change to move them from being blaming to being assertive.

Instead of:	Try this:

Role-Play

The best way to build assertive communication is to practice. You can do this by engaging in role-plays with friends or family members, which provide a great opportunity to work on your nonverbal cues, voice tone, and use of language.

A role-play is a lot like putting on a play at school. You need to come up with some pretend scenarios to try, assign people roles, and take breaks to give each other feedback and work on new skills. One suggestion I always make is to switch roles after a set amount of time so that each person has time to work through each role. This gives everyone a chance to work on their assertiveness skills.

On the next page are a few ideas for role-plays. Spend a few minutes thinking of other scenarios that you might encounter at home, at school, or out in your community. You can add yours to the list. Then find some friends or family members you can practice with, and start role-playing!

ROLE-PLAY!

1. Your parents say you have to leave for school, but you're still searching for your math homework, and you're feeling worried about being late and unprepared.

2. Your friend comes over to your house after school. You want to go out and shoot hoops, but your friend wants to play video games.

3. Your teacher says you didn't turn in your book report, but you're sure that you did.

4. _____

   _____

5. _____

   _____

6. _____

   _____

7. _____

   _____

8. _____

   _____

Nightly Kid News

I'm willing to bet that the nightly news is not your favorite thing to watch on TV, but if you ever do glance at the news, you'll see a lot of assertiveness skills in action. News anchors have to make eye contact with the camera, use an assertive voice, sit tall, and listen to their co-anchors. They have to show confidence through the screen.

Grown-up news might not be very interesting to you, but you can create a nightly kid news show to practice your assertiveness skills! Plan your interesting stories of the day (these might be things you learned about or saw in school), practice reporting on your stories, set up a news desk, and ask your grown-ups to watch your show. Another option is to film your show on a device and replay it for your grown-ups later.

Your show can be five minutes or thirty, every night or just one night a week. As the producer of the show, you get to make the important decisions. Here are some sample news categories:

- The Recess Report

- Sticky Science Situations

- Funny Facts

- Musical Moments

- History Highlights

What will you add to your report?

Sliding into Groups

One communication skill that you need to learn is how to enter a group that's already talking. I call this "sliding into groups." It's an important skill that you'll use throughout your life.

It can feel scary to approach a group that's already formed. You might find yourself having worry thoughts like "What if they don't want me to join?" It's important to remember that groups can make room for more members. When you slide into a group, the group gains a new friend.

Practice these steps with your family to work on your sliding skills.

1 Approach the group.

2 Make eye contact.

3 Listen to the topic.

4 Wait for a break and join the conversation.

ACTIVE LISTENING SKILLS CHECKLIST

An important piece of assertive communication is knowing how to be a good listener. Active listening skills are steps you take to show others that you are paying attention and listening to what they have to say.

This might sound like an easy task, but it's also easy to lose your focus if something isn't interesting to you or you're tired. Review the list of active listening skills here. Check off the ones you already use. Circle the ones you want to practice.

- ❒ Making eye contact with the person speaking
- ❒ Nodding your head to show you're following the story
- ❒ Ignoring distractions around you
- ❒ Asking follow-up questions to understand what the other person has said
- ❒ Standing or sitting up straight
- ❒ Waiting for a break in the conversation before speaking
- ❒ Keeping your comments and questions on topic
- ❒ Using an appropriate voice tone and volume
- ❒ Using nonverbal cues to show interest
- ❒ Giving others a chance to respond
- ❒ Smiling
- ❒ Thinking about what the other person is saying
- ❒ Thinking about how the other person feels
- ❒ Letting the other person finish talking

CHAPTER FIVE

I Believe in Me!

Confident kids are better problem-solvers because they know they have the skills and ability to work through their obstacles. They understand that even though life can feel hard sometimes, they can still do hard things. It's natural to feel more confident in some settings than others. Everyone feels that way. Learning to boost your self-confidence will set you up to conquer even your biggest obstacles.

One important thing to remember is that it takes time to build your self-confidence. If this is something you struggle with right now, you're not alone. Kids are often so busy doing all sorts of "kid things" that they don't always make time to think about their strengths. But it's really helpful to think about what you're good at because it will build you up. Being busy can be fun, but it's also fun to think about how far you've come and where you want to go from here. This builds your self-esteem because it helps you recognize all the hard work and effort you've put in, even when things feel hard.

All About Me Billboard

You know those eye-catching billboards for movies and TV shows that get you excited for new stuff to watch? Those billboards work because they show you that something great is coming soon. And you, too, can create your own personal billboard to show how great you are! Fill in the billboard on the next page with pictures, words, phrases, and even photos to show why you are such a great friend, family member, student, or community member. Showcase your strengths for the world (or anyone you want to show) to see!

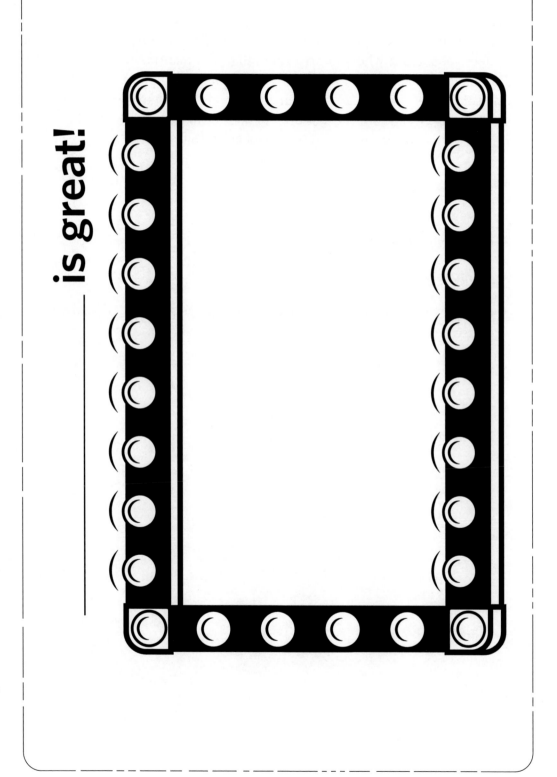

_____ is great!

Tower of Self-Esteem

You can't build your self-esteem overnight, but you can start growing it by thinking about your self-esteem boosters. These are the things you can do or say to feel good about who you are. They might be mantras (like "I can solve hard problems"), happy memories, or even people who support you. There are all kinds of boosters around us. Recognizing them is important. Fill in the tower on the next page by adding one self-esteem booster to each block. See how high your tower gets—you can even add more blocks on your own!

Unsure how to find your own unique boosters? No problem! Here are some categories for inspiration:

- People who support you

- Words or phrases that inspire you to keep trying

- Things you have fun doing (like baking, playing sports, or solving crossword puzzles)

- Things you do that make you feel calm and relaxed

- A favorite memory

- Family traditions

TOWER OF SELF-ESTEEM

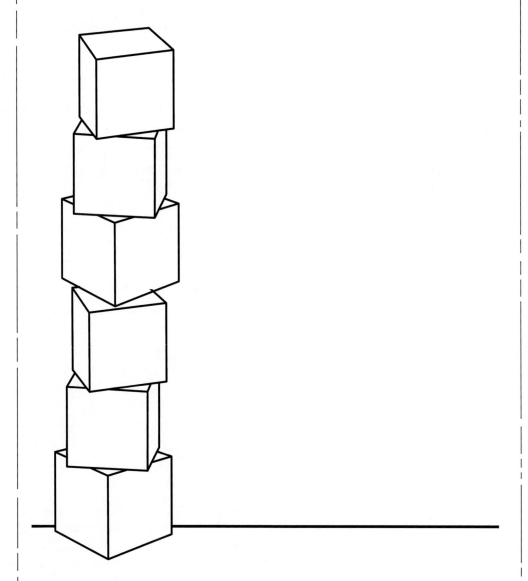

Fill in your self-esteem boosters!

Full Plate of Gratitude

Gratitude involves showing thanks or appreciation for what you have in life. And believe it or not, getting into the habit of expressing gratitude can make you feel happier and more confident. When you take the time to be thankful for what you have, instead of worrying about what you don't have, you're more likely to experience positive emotions.

A simple gratitude strategy you can practice each day is to start the day with three hopeful thoughts and to end the day with three grateful thoughts. When you do this, you start *and* end on a positive note, no matter what happens in between waking up and going to bed.

Another strategy you can use is filling your plate with gratitude. You can use the plate provided on the next page, get your own paper plate, or make one for this exercise. On your plate, write or draw all the things in life that you're thankful for. These can be small things or big things. Update your plate when you think of new things to add!

FULL PLATE OF GRATITUDE

Courage Cards

Although some kids think bravery is the same thing as self-confidence, it's not. You can feel brave one day and not-so-brave another day, but that doesn't mean your self-confidence is gone. The truth is, we all need a little extra courage sometimes. That doesn't make us weak. It simply makes us human!

Your self-confidence grows little by little as you learn and practice new skills, and small acts of courage can be every bit as inspiring as giant acts of bravery. To help you grow your self-confidence, create some courage cards to keep in your backpack. These cards can include positive phrases, words, or drawings to help you work through hard moments.

COURAGE CARDS

You
worked
hard.
You can
do it!

Character Moments

It's easy to get caught up in things like grades or trophies as a sign of success, but those are just things you earn for completing tasks. They don't actually build your self-esteem. You might feel good about winning a trophy for a little while, but eventually it will end up on your shelf and you might even forget it's there.

Character moments, on the other hand, build self-esteem in a strong way. A character moment is a powerful memory of a time when you showcased your positive qualities. Complete the sentences in the worksheet by describing a time when you demonstrated each of the strengths. Then, put the page up on display as a reminder of your great character. You've had so many great moments!

CHARACTER MOMENTS

A *kind* thing I did was

_____.

A *brave* thing I did was

_____.

A *helpful* thing I did was

_____.

Something cool I *created* was

_____.

I was a good *leader* when

_____.

I was a good *problem-solver* when

_____.

I was a good *listener* when

_____.

I was *responsible* when

_____.

I was *honest* when

_____.

I felt *confident* when

_____.

Claps for Me!

It feels really good when other people give us compliments. It's nice to be noticed for our hard work and effort. Most people appreciate getting positive feedback from others.

But did you know that you can actually give yourself positive feedback and get that same boost? When you acknowledge your own hard work and the great things you do, it's like giving yourself a pat on the back. And when you give yourself that much-needed pat, it's a better confidence booster than when someone else gives it to you because this positive feedback becomes part of the way you talk to yourself (known as your *self-talk*).

Your self-talk is really important because it influences how you treat yourself. When you have positive self-talk, you feel good about yourself and believe that you are capable of great things. But when you have negative self-talk, you don't believe in yourself, and all your hard work goes unrecognized.

If you want to truly believe in yourself, you have to begin by recognizing all the good things you do each day. When I was in second grade, I had a teacher who would exclaim, "Claps for you, Katie!" when I worked through something hard. All these years later, I can still picture her smile, but now I've changed the phrase to "Claps for me!" because it's become part of my positive self-talk.

On the next page, write yourself five compliments to help this positive self-talk become a part of who you are. Give yourself some positive feedback—and be specific! The more you do this, the more confident you'll feel.

CLAPS FOR ME!

Look How I Shine

Thinking about your strengths can be hard. A lot of kids even tell me they feel uncomfortable when I ask them to do that. It can be difficult for kids to think about their strengths because they are often told to avoid bragging or showing off. Adults are always telling them to downplay their strengths and achievements so other kids won't feel bad.

When you're in a group setting, bragging about how great you are might make some kids feel resentful or like they don't measure up. If you do this a lot, kids might stop listening. But there's a big difference between sharing your strengths and bragging about your achievements.

Think about what it's like when you play on a team. It takes all kinds of talents to make up a great soccer team. You need people who can score goals, people who can play defense, and someone who is brave enough to play goalie. Check out the two statements below. Which statement sounds like someone who is sharing their strengths? Put a happy face next to that one. Which one sounds like someone who is bragging? Put a sad face next to that one.

"I play goalie really well. Is it okay if I start in the goal?"

"I always score the most goals, so I should only play forward."

Do you see the difference between sharing your strengths and bragging about your achievements? On the next page, list the ways you shine under each category. This will help you think about how you can use your strengths to reach your goals.

LOOK HOW I SHINE

My brain does this for me:

- _____
- _____
- _____

I am a good friend because:

- _____
- _____
- _____

I'm unique because:

- _____
- _____
- _____

My body does this for me:

- _____
- _____
- _____

SELF-ESTEEM CHECK-IN

This is a good time to do a quick check-in to see how you're feeling about yourself. Focus on how you feel today, and circle the response that most closely corresponds with how you're feeling. Remember that everyone has ups and downs, so it's okay if you're feeling uncertain about some of these.

1.	I am a good friend.	Always	Sometimes	Never
2.	I am responsible.	Always	Sometimes	Never
3.	I am kind to others.	Always	Sometimes	Never
4.	I am a good listener.	Always	Sometimes	Never
5.	I am creative.	Always	Sometimes	Never
6.	I can solve problems.	Always	Sometimes	Never
7.	I help others.	Always	Sometimes	Never
8.	I believe in myself.	Always	Sometimes	Never
9.	I know I can reach my goals.	Always	Sometimes	Never
10.	I feel happy and confident.	Always	Sometimes	Never
11.	People can count on me.	Always	Sometimes	Never
12.	I am a hard worker.	Always	Sometimes	Never

Which of these things do you feel very confident about?

_____

Which of these things do you want to work on? _____

_____

How can you work on those things? _____

_____

What Can I Say Instead?

Have you ever experienced self-doubt? That happens when you feel stressed and you start thinking that you're not capable of doing the things you want to do. Self-doubt can sneak up on you and make you feel less confident.

Remember that the way you talk to yourself (your *self-talk*) shapes how you think about yourself. If you have a lot of self-doubt thoughts, then you'll feel like you're not capable. But if you think confident thoughts, then you'll feel like you can do anything. To help you reframe your self-doubt thoughts, fill in the thought bubbles here to come up with alternative statements that help you be more confident.

WHAT CAN I SAY INSTEAD?

I have no friends.

I should quit.

This is impossible.

I'm not good at this.

A Note to Self

When you have a hard day, it helps to write yourself a note reminding you that bad days are temporary and that you can do things differently next time. Writing helps you get your feelings out, and it also gives you a chance to forgive yourself and to create a plan to start again. Everyone has hard days, but your hard days will never define you.

To create your letter, fill in the blanks on the next page, or write a letter of your own. This will help you work through your hard day and figure out how to start fresh tomorrow.

A NOTE TO SELF

Dear _____,

Today was hard because _____.

When this happened, I felt _____.

I handled this situation by _____,

but I wish I had _____ instead.

It's okay that today was a hard day. It's okay if I made mistakes. One thing that did go well today was _____.

When that happened, I felt _____.

Tomorrow is a new day. Tomorrow I will begin the day by thinking these three positive thoughts about myself:

1. _____

2. _____

3. _____

I learned this important lesson today: _____

_____.

If I have a similar problem tomorrow, I will _____

_____.

Love, _____

CHAPTER SIX

Think Positive!

Positive thinking helps us work through our negative thoughts, focus on our goals, and decrease stress. But positive thinking isn't just about saying positive things. It's about shifting your *mindset* (which is your way of looking at the world) so you know that you *can* feel happy again, even on your hardest days.

No one is happy or positive every second of every day. We all experience a lot of emotions each day. That's part of being human. But when you have a positive mindset, it protects you from getting stuck in negative thoughts or feelings of hopelessness. When kids are able to use a positive mindset, they are better able to cope with stress and solve their own problems.

Flip It!

To begin shifting your mindset, it helps to understand how positive and negative thinking work. Many kids don't know that negative thinking is really powerful. It actually takes three positive thoughts to overpower one negative thought. Another important fact: The first step to positive thinking actually involves listening to your negative thoughts. All thoughts try to tell us important things. It's up to us to listen. Let's try it!

In the first box on the next page, draw a picture that shows the negative thoughts that are weighing you down. Be sure to draw them in detail. In the second box, draw a relaxing scene while you pause and practice some deep breathing. In the third box, draw yourself using three positive thoughts to work through the negative ones. These are alternative ways of thinking that help you learn and grow. That's three steps to change your thinking!

FLIP IT!

① Draw your negative thoughts here.

② Breathe and create a relaxing scene.

③ Draw yourself using three positive thoughts here.

CHANGE COURSE

We all make mistakes. When you make a mistake, it doesn't mean that you are a failure or that you can't overcome something. Mistakes actually teach us what we can change next time so we can overcome something hard.

In the Past box, write down a failure or mistake that's bugging you. Take some time to think about why it might have happened. Add those details in there. In the Present box, write down what you can do differently next time so you don't make that same mistake twice. That's called *changing your course*. You're correcting and trying a new strategy!

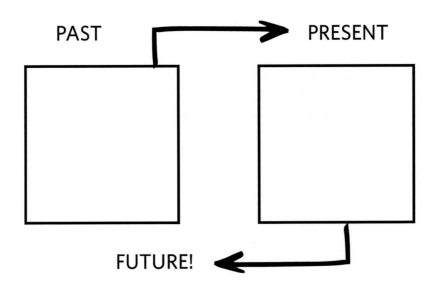

PAST → PRESENT

FUTURE! ←

Swipe Up!

One fun thing about technology is that if you dislike something or aren't interested in it for some reason, you can just swipe up to the next thing. It's an instant change.

Changing your thinking isn't quite as simple, so if you find that you get caught up in negative or worry thoughts a lot, change won't happen with a single swipe. It will take some practice and some repeated "swiping up" to keep those negative thoughts from cluttering your mind. But with continued practice and effort, you can learn to swipe up and pop a positive thought into your mind whenever you're having a hard time. All you need is your imagination!

First, you need to bank some positive thoughts. Think of some phrases, thoughts, or things that make you feel confident. Try to fill your positive thought bank with as many of these thoughts as you can. You can always continue to add to it later.

Then on the next page, practice swiping up. On the first screen, write or draw a negative or worry thought that feels heavy in your mind. On the second screen, swipe up for one of your positive thoughts.

Positive Thought Bank

SWIPE UP!

Negative Thought   Positive Alternative

Visualize Success

Visualization is a powerful tool that can help you focus your attention on good things to come. The word *visualize* is just another way of saying that you can imagine something in your mind. By closing your eyes, using deep breathing, and visualizing positive outcomes, you actually set yourself up to try your best. Professional athletes use this handy tool, and the best part is, you can do it anywhere.

If you're having a hard day, or you're just expecting that it will take a lot of work to reach your goal, follow these steps:

- Close your eyes and take three slow breaths.

- In your mind, draw a picture of your best version of you. Are you trying to reach a goal of some kind? Great! Picture all the steps you'll take to reach it.

- Open your eyes and draw your visualization. You can use the box on the next page.

- Find step one in your drawing. Start there!

VISUALIZE SUCCESS

"I Can" Stickies

Part of making positive thinking work for you involves focusing your attention on what you *know* you can do. This is known as focusing on your comfort zone. There will be times when you want to stretch yourself outside of your comfort zone to learn new things, but when you know what you do well and where you shine, it will help you tap into positive thinking when you do encounter obstacles.

When you talk about yourself in a positive way, you feel good about yourself. It's like you are your own cheering section. Cheering yourself on also empowers you to work through hard things on your own because you don't *need* a teacher, coach, or other grown-up to tell you that you can do it—you know it in your heart, and that pushes you to keep going.

Fill in the "sticky notes" on the next page with things you know you can do well. You might write, "I can be a good friend" or "I can do my homework on my own." When you fill this page with all that you can do, you'll see that you have a lot of skills to solve problems.

If you want to take this activity to the next level, get some actual sticky notes, fill them with positive thoughts about yourself, and post them in your bedroom. This will give you a daily visual reminder of all the great things you are capable of doing!

"I CAN" STICKIES

I can solve problems!

Thought Rating Scale

It's easy to get into patterns of thinking where one thought plays in your mind over and over again. It's like having a sticky thought that you can't get unstuck from! This happens to a lot of kids. It might be because you're focusing on something that makes you feel stressed or worried or because you're uncertain about something and your mind is anticipating the worst. Either way, it helps to pinpoint the sticky thought, rate how useful it is, and think of helpful alternatives.

In this activity, you'll consider all kinds of thoughts, positive and negative, and determine how useful they are in helping you through a stressful situation. You'll use this scale to rate the usefulness of each thought:

0 = Not at all useful
1 = Not very useful
2 = Somewhat useful
3 = Useful
4 = Very useful
5 = This is good thinking!

For example, let's say you're worried about your softball game because two players on your team won't be there. The thought that keeps running through your mind is "We don't stand a chance. We'll never win this game." Here's what your ratings might look like:

Sticky thought rating: 0

Why? This is negative thinking and makes me feel helpless.

Alternative thought: If we all work together and try new positions, we can do our best.

New thought rating: 5

Why? This is positive thinking with problem solving.

Your turn! On the next page, work through some of your sticky thoughts.

THOUGHT RATING SCALE

Scenario: _____

Sticky thought: _____

Thought rating: _____

Why? _____

Alternative thought: _____

New thought rating: _____

Why? _____

Scenario: _____

Sticky thought: _____

Thought rating: _____

Why? _____

Alternative thought: _____

New thought rating: _____

Why? _____

Scenario: _____

Sticky thought: _____

Thought rating: _____

Why? _____

Alternative thought: _____

New thought rating: _____

Why? _____

Win/Loss Ratio

Remember the 3:1 positive-to-negative thought ratio that was mentioned at the beginning of this chapter? In other words, it takes three positive thoughts to overpower one negative thought. That's important because it reminds us that we can conquer negative thinking by refocusing our brains on positive thoughts—but we just need more positives to outweigh the negatives.

One way to do this is to think of your win/loss ratio for the day. Let's say you got frustrated at school twice today: You argued with a friend at recess, and later your teacher redirected you for not listening in class. Those are two little losses for the day because you felt frustrated. Now let's think of all the little wins you had today. Did you start the day with your favorite breakfast? Did something funny happen at school? Did you get to play with your friends at recess? To help you overpower negative thinking, you can add up your wins for the day (no matter how small!) and compare them to your losses to see how the positives outweigh the negatives.

To try this out for yourself, use the win/loss ratio sheet on the next page. Add up all your wins in the first column and all your losses in the second column. This is a great activity to do as part of your bedtime routine because it helps you focus on the positive parts of your day and lets you realize that even on a hard day, there are good moments.

WIN/LOSS RATIO

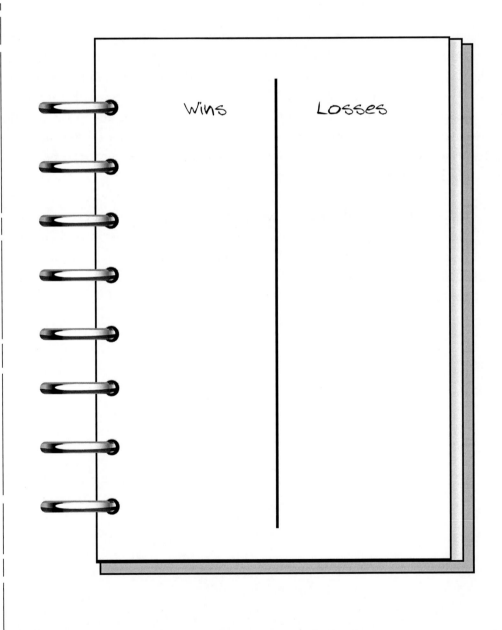

Wins | Losses

Small Steps to Goals

One thing a lot of kids tell me is that they have very specific goals that they want to reach right away. It's common for kids to want to shift from a cool idea ("I want to be on a baking show!") to the finish line ("I'm on a baking show!"). But the truth is that reaching goals is usually a slow process, and it takes a positive mindset to persist through the stumbling blocks along the way.

I like to think of setting goals as taking a journey along a path that requires a lot of small steps, like walking through a forest. If you race from beginning to end, you'll miss all the beauty and interesting things the forest has to offer. But if you slow down and take small steps, you'll see a whole world you didn't even know existed.

Think about a goal you have. Let's say your goal is to paint a beautiful sunset like one you saw on a postcard. What are all the steps you have to take to meet that goal? Do you need painting lessons? Do you need to sketch first? Do you need to learn how to mix colors? All of those small steps are called *benchmarks*. Those are the mini-goals that help you reach your big goal.

You can have as many benchmarks as you need, but it's good to think of at least three you need to take to reach your goal. This helps you break down your goal into manageable parts so that it doesn't feel overwhelming.

Try it out for yourself! Pick a goal you'd like to work out, and then identify three benchmarks (or small steps) you can take to get there.

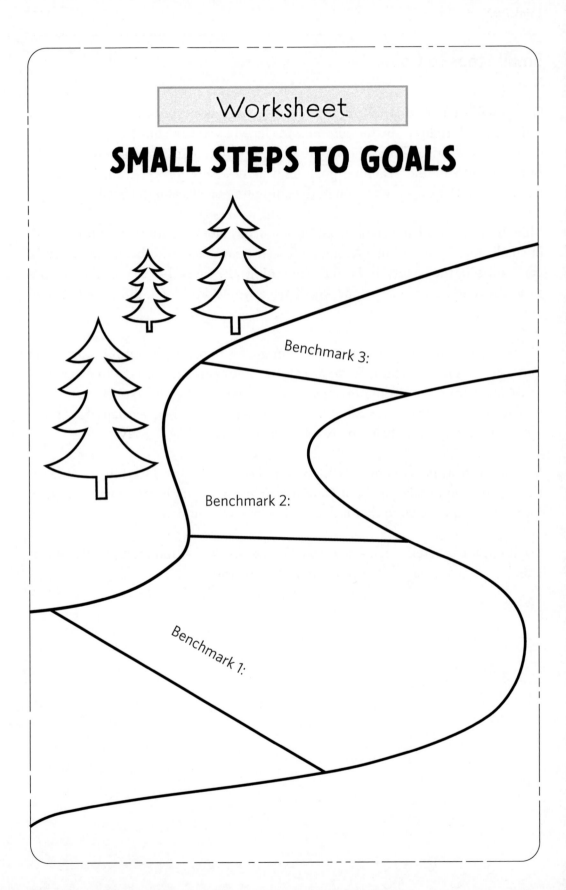

Positive Thought Chain

The great thing about positive thinking is that it tends to inspire more positive thinking. Once you get into the habit of thinking about the things that make you feel confident, capable, and happy, you'll notice that one good thought leads to another. Of course, the same is true for negative thinking. In either case, you can end up in a cycle. A *cycle* is something that keeps repeating itself in a loop, kind of like the wheel on a bicycle going around and around.

To start a positive thought chain, start small. If starting small feels like a theme in this chapter, it's for good reason. Stress can occur when we pile pressure on ourselves, even positive pressure. Setting a ton of goals might seem healthy, but we have to learn to balance goals with downtime. We have to balance exciting activities with calming activities. We have to feel gratitude for all things, big and small.

A small positive thought might sound like "I believe in myself." Think about that for a moment. What does that mean? Let's break it down. It might mean "I know I am a hard worker," "I am capable of reaching my goals," "I always try my best," "I am thoughtful and caring," "I am good at making friends," or lots of other things. One positive thought can generate more positive thoughts when we start a positive thought chain.

Your turn! On the next page, fill in the positive thought chain. If you get stuck, that's okay. Close your eyes and imagine something positive about yourself. There's your next thought!

Extra tip: This is a fun game to play in a group. One person starts the chain by sharing a positive thought, the person next to them shares a positive thought related to the original thought, and you keep going around the group until you link back to the person who started it!

POSITIVE THOUGHT CHAIN

Think of one positive thought for each link in the chain!

One Last Grounding Exercise

It's always a good idea to work on a grounding exercise when you're calm so you know how to use it when you're upset. Grounding exercises help kids cope with stressful situations by staying present in the moment.

Stress and worry can make you feel like you can't catch your breath. Sometimes frustration feels this way too. Grounding yourself in your surroundings will help you work through those uncomfortable emotions and reframe your thinking.

Follow these steps to try a simple grounding exercise:

- Put your feet on the ground—stand up if you can.

- Take a slow breath (in for four, hold for four, out for four, hold for four).

- Repeat.

- Name three things you can see, three things you can hear, three things you can feel, and three things you can smell.

- Take another slow breath.

- Say, "I am okay. I am calming down."

- Name three things that make you smile.

Practice this once a day, even if you don't need it, to train your brain to work through difficult moments. The more you try this strategy when you're calm, the easier it is to use when you feel overwhelmed.

Final Thoughts

Whether you finished this book or skipped ahead to see how it ends (that's okay—I do that sometimes too), congratulations on working to build your stress-buster skills!

Stress is a part of life, and not all stress will send you running for a book like this. But learning how to sit with discomfort and cope with stress is an important part of life that you won't learn in school.

Take your time with this book. Revisit the strategies that you found most helpful. Teach them to a sibling or friend. My hope is that this book will inspire kids to empathize with each other, help each other out during hard moments, and work together to overcome obstacles of all sizes. One thing I know for certain is that when kids work together, everybody wins.

STRESS-BUSTER
CERTIFICATE

This is to certify that

_____

has learned to cope with stress, work through hard things, and use positive thinking. Way to go!

Katie Hurley, LCSW

_____
Katie Hurley, LCSW
The Stress-Buster Workbook for Kids Author

For your convenience, purchasers can download and print
the worksheets from www.pesi.com/StressBusters

FURTHER READING

Books for Kids

Calm and Peaceful Mindful Me: A Mindfulness How-To Guide for Toddlers and Kids
by **Andrea Dorn**
This book helps young children learn to use mindfulness with a beautiful narrative and
tips and scripts throughout.

Coping Skills Workbook for Kids by **Janine Halloran**
This workbook includes over seventy-five activities to learn to cope with stress,
anxiety, and anger.

Empathy Is Your Superpower: A Book About Understanding the Feelings of Others
by **Cori Bussolari and Zach Grzeszkowiak**
This illustrated guide helps kids understand what it means to care about the thoughts
and feelings of others, and how to do it.

Find Your Calm: A Mindful Approach to Relieve Anxiety and Grow Your Bravery
by **Gabi Garcia and Marta Pineda**
This book helps kids learn how to use mindfulness to cope with feelings of anxiety.

Wemberly Worried by **Kevin Henkes**
Wemberly worries about everything: big things, little things, and all the things in
between. When Wemberly attends her first day of school, she learns that she is not
alone and that she can work through her worries with friends.

Wilma Jean the Worry Machine by **Julia Cook**
Wilma Jean describes the physical feelings of worry and anxiety and learns how to
overcome them by getting help from a teacher.

Books for Parents

Beyond Behaviors: Using Brain Science and Compassion to Understand and Solve Children's Behavioral Challenges by **Mona Delahooke**
This book redefines the concept of problem behaviors and helps parents learn to view challenging moments as connection-seeking moments.

Happy Campers: 9 Summer Camp Secrets for Raising Kids Who Become Thriving Adults by **Audrey Monke**
Packed with specific exercises to use at home, this book helps parents understand what kids need to build connections, independence, and resilience.

The Happy Kid Handbook: How to Raise Joyful Children in a Stressful World by **Katie Hurley**
This book breaks down the stress and anxiety that kids of all ages face and offers practical tips to help parents help their kids find happiness, no matter their obstacles.

The Power of Showing Up: How Parental Presence Shapes Who Our Kids Become and How Their Brains Get Wired by **Daniel Siegel and Tina Payne Bryson**
Focused on the four S's—safe, seen, soothed, and secure—this book gets back to the basics to help parents build positive and lasting connections with their kids.

Thrivers: The Surprising Reasons Why Some Kids Struggle and Others Shine by **Michele Borba**
This book explores the research on resilience and gives parents tools to use to help their kids learn to thrive.

ACKNOWLEDGMENTS

One thing kids don't often learn until they're much older is that it takes a team of people to publish a book! It's true. Even authors make mistakes, but other people on the team catch those mistakes and help the author fix them.

Thank you to Karsyn Morse at PESI Publishing for making this idea become a reality. I've wanted to write a book for kids for a LONG time. I needed the right person to help me make it happen.

A giant thank-you is in order to the editors (the mistake catchers!) of this book, Jenessa Jackson and Gretchen Panzer.

Before an idea becomes a book, the author needs to do some research. Thank you to my research assistant and intern, Kira Patel, for helping me prepare to write this book.

Finally, my family always cheers me on and reads my writing along the way to help me write the best book possible (even my kids!). Thanks to Liam, Riley, Sean, and even our dog, Sugar, for filling me up with positivity while I wrote this book.